McDougal Littell
Pre-Algebra

Larson   Boswell   Kanold   Stiff

CHAPTER 1

Resource Book

The Resource Book contains a wide variety of blackline masters available for Chapter 1. The blacklines are organized by lesson. Included are support materials for the teacher as well as practice, activities, applications, and project resources.

McDougal Littell
A DIVISION OF HOUGHTON MIFFLIN COMPANY
Evanston, Illinois • Boston • Dallas

Contributing Authors

The authors wish to thank **Jessica Pflueger** for her contributions to the Chapter 1 Resource Book.

ISBN-13: 978-0-618-26936-5   ISBN-10: 0-618-26936-3

56789-DOM-09 08 07

Contents

1 Variables, Expressions, and Integers

Contents

Contents

Descriptions of Resources

This Chapter Resource Book is organized by lessons within the chapter in order to make your planning easier. The following materials are provided:

Tips for New Teachers   These teaching notes provide both new and experienced teachers with useful teaching tips for each lesson, including tips about common errors and inclusion.

Parents as Partners   This guide helps parents contribute to student success by providing an overview of the chapter along with questions and activities for parents and students to work on together.

Lesson Plans and Lesson Plans for Block Scheduling   This planning template helps teachers select the materials they will use to teach each lesson from among the variety of materials available for the lesson. The block-scheduling version provides additional information about pacing.

Activity Masters   These blackline masters make it easier for students to record their work on selected activities in the Student Edition, or they provide alternative activities for selected lessons.

Technology Activities with Keystrokes   Keystrokes for various models of calculators are provided for each Technology Activity in the Student Edition where appropriate, along with alternative Technology Activities for selected lessons.

Practice A, B, and C   These exercises offer additional practice for the material in each lesson, including application problems. There are three levels of practice for each lesson: A (basic), B (average), and C (advanced).

Study Guide   These two pages provide additional instruction, worked-out examples, and practice exercises covering the key concepts and vocabulary in each lesson.

Real-World Problem Solving   These exercises offer problem-solving activities for the material in selected lessons in a real world context.

Challenge Practice   These exercises offer challenging practice on the mathematics of each lesson for advanced students.

Chapter Review Games and Activities   This worksheet offers fun practice at the end of the chapter and provides an alternative way to review the chapter content in preparation for the Chapter Test.

Projects with Rubric   These projects allow students to delve more deeply into a problem that applies the mathematics of the chapter. Teacher's notes and a 4-point rubric are included. The projects include a real-life project, a cooperative project, and an independent extra credit project.

Cumulative Practice   These practice pages help students maintain skills from the current chapter and preceding chapters.

Tips for New Teachers

For use with Chapter 1

Lesson 1.1

TEACHING TIP Remind students that numerical expressions and variable expressions do not involve equals signs. Only equations have equals signs.

TEACHING TIP Before presenting the Common Words and Phrases that Indicate Operations chart on page 6, have students brainstorm in small groups words that indicate these operations. Then on chart paper or on the board, list all the brainstormed words and phrases. Finally, compare the brainstormed words and phrases to the chart on page 6. Have students check to see if they came up with any additional words or phrases or if they omitted some of those in the chart. An alternative activity would be to have a chart posted for each operation and to have students write terms on post-its and place these terms on the charts.

TEACHING TIP This lesson discusses a number of ways and symbols that indicate multiplication and division. You may wish to have students create a chart showing these various methods. Students should take note of the two Reading Algebra suggestions on pages 5 and 6 regarding the $\times$ and $\div$ symbols.

Lesson 1.2

COMMON ERROR Remind students that in exponential expressions, the exponent shows the number of times the base is used as a factor. The exponent itself does not get multiplied by the base. To help students avoid this common error, show them that 2^3 is equal to 8, not 6.

TEACHING TIP In Exercise 4 on page 12, students are asked to evaluate an exponential expression with a decimal base. Encourage students to do this multiplication in a step-by-step manner so that they can see that the product will require three decimal places, including a zero as a place holder. Also point out that when a positive decimal (or fraction) is raised to a power, the result is *less* than the original base.

Student Reference: A Problem Solving Plan

TEACHING TIP You may wish to create a poster to hang in your classroom that displays the four steps described in the A Problem Solving Plan box on page 14. Have students refer to this plan frequently when solving problems.

INCLUSION You may wish to let students use photocopied sheets or black line masters for word problems so that they can underline or highlight the important words as part of the Read and Understand step.

TEACHING TIP Be sure that students do not skip Step 4 of the Problem Solving Plan and that they carefully and thoughtfully check their solutions to see that they are both reasonable and labeled correctly.

Lesson 1.3

COMMON ERROR When using a mnemonic such as Please Excuse My Dear Aunt Sally to remember order of operations, some students may do all multiplications before all divisions and all additions before all subtractions. Be sure that students understand that multiplication and division are of the same rank and therefore are simplified in straightforward left-to-right order. The same is true for addition and subtraction.

TEACHING TIP Stress to students that a fraction bar acts as a grouping symbol. The numerator and denominator are first simplified separately; then the final operation is the division indicated by the fraction bar. If students are using a calculator, be sure that they insert the necessary parentheses to ensure the correct answer. Along these lines, it may be worthwhile to spend some time to instruct students how to use the functions of a calculator correctly as they pertain to the order of operations. If students are using individual, different calculators, you may wish to provide examples that will filter out any improper calculator use.

Tips for New Teachers

For use with Chapter 1

Lesson 1.4

TEACHING TIP Be sure to emphasize the differences between *opposite*, *absolute value*, and *opposite of absolute value*. For example, $-(-3) = 3$, $|-3| = 3$, and $-|-3| = -3$. Stress that since absolute value is never negative, the opposite of an absolute value is never positive.

COMMON ERROR Some students routinely assume an answer is negative if they see a negative sign at the beginning of an exercise. For instance, in Example 4a on page 24 be sure students understand that when evaluating $-y$ they are looking for the opposite of whatever value y is. As the example shows, this does not mean that the answer ultimately will be negative.

Lesson 1.5

INCLUSION When teaching the addition of integers, you may wish to introduce two-color counters and allow students to use them for as long as they feel they need to.

TEACHING TIP When adding integers, you may wish to use the following alliterations as mnemonic devices: **s**ame sign **s**um, and **d**ifferent sign **d**ifference.

COMMON ERROR Some students may assume that the statement in Exercise 59 on page 33 is always true. Point out that if a and b have opposite signs, then $|a + b|$ does *not* equal $|a| + |b|$.

Lesson 1.6

TEACHING TIP Insist that students rewrite all subtractions of integers as additions. Although some subtractions may be performed using mental calculations, in most cases students will need to be proficient with this skill to limit the number of errors.

COMMON ERROR When rewriting a subtraction of integers expressions as addition, be sure that students do *not* change the sign of the first number.

COMMON ERROR In Checkpoint Exercise 8 on page 35, be certain when students substitute -14 for y that they write the expression as $-9 - (-14)$, rather than $-9 - 14$.

Lesson 1.7

INCLUSION You may wish to introduce multiplication of integers by showing the process as multiple additions, perhaps by using two-color counters. For example, $3(-2)$ can be shown as $(-2) + (-2) + (-2)$.

TEACHING TIP Be sure that students understand that the sign rules are the same for multiplication and division of integers. You may wish to provide students with the table below for their reference.

×, ÷	+	−
+	+	−
−	−	+

Lesson 1.8

TEACHING TIP Remind students that the quadrants are numbered in *counterclockwise*, not clockwise, order.

TEACHING TIP Point out to students that every point whose ordered pair contains a zero will be located *on* an axis. If the zero is first, the point will be on the y-axis. If the zero is second, the point will be on the x-axis.

Name _____ Date _____

1 Parents as Partners

For use with Chapter 1

Chapter Overview One way you can help your student succeed in Chapter 1 is by discussing the lesson goals in the chart below. When a lesson is completed, ask your student the following questions. "What were the goals of the lesson? What new words and formulas did you learn? How can you apply the ideas of the lesson to your life?"

Lesson Title	Lesson Goals	Key Applications
1.1: Expressions and Variables	Evaluate and write variable expressions.	• Blue Whales • Astronauts • Music Competition • DVD Rentals
1.2: Powers and Exponents	Use powers to describe repeated multiplication.	• Ice Sculpture • Gift Box • E-mail • Aquariums
1.3: Order of Operations	Use order of operations to evaluate expressions.	• Flower Flag • Twin Convention • Plants • Digital Cameras
1.4: Comparing and Ordering Integers	Compare and order integers.	• Supercooled Insects • Volcanoes • Neptune's Moons • Underwater Cities
1.5: Adding Integers	Add integers.	• Scuba Diver • Food Science • Hockey • Lake Vostok
1.6: Subtracting Integers	Subtract integers.	• The Big Dig • Ice Cream Production • Chemistry • Avalanches
1.7: Multiplying and Dividing Integers	Multiply and divide integers.	• Antarctic Temperatures • Electronics • MIR Submersible • Free Diving
1.8: The Coordinate Plane	Identify and plot points in a coordinate plane.	• Fish • Earth Science • Fuel Economy

Notetaking Strategies

Keeping a Notebook is the strategy featured in Chapter 1 (see page 4). Encourage your student to include assignments, formulas, rules and properties, vocabulary, symbols, and worked-out examples in his/her notebook. Remind your student that it may be helpful to draw a diagram when he/she copies examples into his/her notebook. Also, he/she should include comments that make the solution process clear to help him/her study for an exam.

CHAPTER
1
Continued

Name _____ Date _____

Parents as Partners

For use with Chapter 1

Key Ideas Your student can demonstrate understanding of key concepts by working through the following exercises with you.

Lesson	Exercise
1.1	You can evaluate the expression $8n$ to find the amount spent on 8 notebooks. Find the amount spent if each notebook costs $2.50.
1.2	Evaluate the expression when $m = 4$ and $m = 0.4$. **a.** m^2 **b.** m^3 **c.** m^4
1.3	Evaluate the expression $\dfrac{2y^2 - 5}{x + 8}$ when $x = 1$ and $y = 5$.
1.4	The daily low temperatures (°C) for one week in December in Fargo, North Dakota are given below. Order the temperatures from least to greatest. $-15, -20, -13, -14, -22, -11, -21$
1.5	Find the sum. **a.** $-15 + (-24)$ **b.** $30 + (-57)$ **c.** $-9 + 18$
1.6	Evaluate the expression when $d = -3$. **a.** $d - 7$ **b.** $-11 - d$ **c.** $d - 13 - 21$
1.7	Find the product or quotient. **a.** $-9(-17)$ **b.** $112 \div (-8)$
1.8	What is the y-coordinate of the point $(-5, 5)$?

Home Involvement Activity

Directions: Make a coordinate grid of your neighborhood. Use the front door to your house or apartment building as the origin. Plot the objects found in your neighborhood, such as a mailbox, trees, or a park. Use the number of steps you take to each object as the units. Use left, right, forward, and backward as the directions you walk to each object to find the object's coordinates. Keep the scale of the grid in mind. Label each point with its coordinates and state the quadrant the object lies in.

Answers:

1.1: $20 **1.2: a.** 16; 0.16 **b.** 64; 0.064 **c.** 256; 0.0256 **1.3:** 5
1.4: $-22, -21, -20, -15, -14, -13, -11$ **1.5: a.** -39 **b.** -27 **c.** 9
1.6: a. -10 **b.** -8 **c.** -37 **1.7: a.** 153 **b.** -14 **1.8:** 5

LESSON

1.1

Teacher's Name _____ Class _____ Room _____ Date _____

Lesson Plan

1-day lesson (See *Pacing and Assignment Guide*, TE page 2A)
For use with pages 5–9

GOAL   Evaluate and write variable expressions.

State/Local Objectives _____

_____

✓ **Check the items you wish to use for this lesson.**

STARTING OPTIONS

_____   Warm-Up: Transparencies

TEACHING OPTIONS

_____   Notetaking Guide

_____   Examples: 1–3, SE pages 5–6

_____   Extra Examples: TE page 6

_____   Checkpoint Exercises: 1–4, SE page 6

_____   Technology Activity: CRB page 7

_____   Concept Check: TE page 6

_____   Guided Practice Exercises: 1–11, SE page 7

APPLY/HOMEWORK

Homework Assignment

_____   Basic: pp. 7–9 Exs. 12–27, 32–43, 49, 50, 57–67

_____   Average: pp. 7–9 Exs. 16–27, 32–38, 40, 45–55, 57–67

_____   Advanced: pp. 7–9 Exs. 16–19, 28–56*, 59–67

Reteaching the Lesson

_____   Practice: CRB pages 8–10 (Level A, Level B, Level C); Practice Workbook

_____   Study Guide: CRB pages 11–12; Spanish Study Guide

Extending the Lesson

_____   Challenge: SE page 9; CRB page 13

ASSESSMENT OPTIONS

_____   Daily Quiz (1.1): TE page 9 or Transparencies

_____   Standardized Test Practice: SE page 9

Notes _____

_____

_____

_____

LESSON
1.1

Lesson Plan for Block Scheduling

Half-block lesson (See *Pacing and Assignment Guide*, TE page 2A)

For use with pages 5–9

GOAL   **Evaluate and write variable expressions.**

State/Local Objectives _____

_____

Lesson 1.1

✓ **Check the items you wish to use for this lesson.**

STARTING OPTIONS

_____ Warm-Up: Transparencies

TEACHING OPTIONS

_____ Notetaking Guide

_____ Examples: 1–3, SE pages 5–6

_____ Extra Examples: TE page 6

_____ Checkpoint Exercises: 1–4, SE page 6

_____ Technology Activity: CRB page 7

_____ Concept Check: TE page 6

_____ Guided Practice Exercises: 1–11, SE page 7

Chapter Pacing Guide	
Day	**Lesson**
1	**1.1**; 1.2
2	1.3; 1.4
3	1.5; 1.6
4	1.7; 1.8
5	Ch. 1 Review and Projects

APPLY/HOMEWORK

Homework Assignment

_____ Block Schedule: pp. 7–9 Exs. 16–27, 32–38, 40, 45–55, 57–67 (with 1.2)

Reteaching the Lesson

_____ Practice: CRB pages 8–10 (Level A, Level B, Level C); Practice Workbook

_____ Study Guide: CRB pages 11–12; Spanish Study Guide

Extending the Lesson

_____ Challenge: SE page 9; CRB page 13

ASSESSMENT OPTIONS

_____ Daily Quiz (1.1): TE page 9 or Transparencies

_____ Standardized Test Practice: SE page 9

Notes _____

_____

_____

_____

_____

Name _____ Date _____

1.1 Technology Activity

For use with pages 5–9

GOAL Use a calculator to evaluate variable expressions.

EXAMPLE In a recent year, the average American used about 708 pounds of fruit and vegetables. Use a verbal model to write a variable expression to find the number of pounds of fruit and vegetables used per person per month.

Solution

Let m represent the number of months. The word *per* indicates division.

Pounds of fruit and vegetables used per person per month	=	Pounds of fruit and vegetables used per person per year	÷	Number of months

$$= 708 \div m$$

The number of pounds of fruit and vegetables used per person per month is given by the expression $708 \div m$, or $\dfrac{708}{m}$. You can use your calculator to evaluate this expression when $m = 12$.

Keystrokes   **Display**

708 ÷ 12 =   59

Answer: The number of pounds of fruit and vegetables used per person per month is 59 pounds.

DRAW CONCLUSIONS Use a calculator to evaluate the expression when $x = 24$.

1. $x + 179$

2. $257 - x$

3. $11x$

4. $\dfrac{708}{x}$

5. $2.5x$

6. $\dfrac{x}{1.5}$

7. A farmer's organization predicts that in a future year, the average American will use about 780 pounds of fruit and vegetables. Find the number of pounds of fruit and vegetables used per person (a) per month and (b) per week.

Name _____ Date _____

Practice A

For use with pages 5–9

Evaluate the expression when $x = 5$.

1. $x + 6$ **2.** $21 - x$ **3.** $9x$ **4.** $\dfrac{20}{x}$

5. $12 + x$ **6.** $36 - x$ **7.** $10x$ **8.** $\dfrac{35}{x}$

Evaluate the expression when $a = 4$ and $b = 3$.

9. $a - b$ **10.** $a + 6$ **11.** ab **12.** $\dfrac{9}{b}$

13. $\dfrac{28}{a}$ **14.** $7b$ **15.** $64 - b$ **16.** $13 + a$

Write a variable expression to represent the phrase.

17. The sum of a number and 7   **18.** 11 fewer than a number

19. The quotient of a number and 6   **20.** A number times 8

21. 5 less than a number   **22.** 5 divided into a number

23. You can evaluate the expression $112 - p$ to find the number of pencils you have left from a package of 112 pencils after you have distributed p pencils among your classmates. Find the number of pencils left over after distributing 56 pencils.

24. You buy 5 shirts each having the same price. Write a variable expression for the total amount you spend on the shirts. How much money do you spend on the shirts when each shirt costs $15?

In Exercises 25–27, use the double bar graph that shows three teams' scores in an academic competition. A team's final score is the sum of the points for the verbal section v and the math section m.

25. Write a variable expression for a team's final score.

26. Find each team's final score.

27. Another team earns 175 points in the verbal section. At least how many points must the team earn in the math section to have a higher final score than teams A, B, and C?

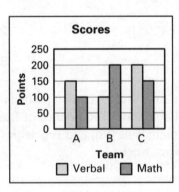

Name _____ Date _____

Practice B

For use with pages 5–9

Evaluate the expression when y = 6.

1. $\frac{24}{y}$

2. $5y$

3. $20 - y$

4. $19 + y$

5. $y + 13$

6. $54 - y$

7. $7y$

8. $\frac{36}{y}$

Evaluate the expression when m = 7, n = 9, and q = 10.

9. nq

10. $\frac{18}{n}$

11. $m + q$

12. $29 - m$

13. $58 - m$

14. $41 + n$

15. $16q$

16. $\frac{36}{n}$

17. You are dividing 130 students into g equally sized groups for a field trip. Write a variable expression to find the number of students in each group.

Write a variable expression to represent the phrase.

18. A number added to 27

19. 29 decreased by a number

20. 6 fewer than a number

21. The sum of 16 and a number

22. The product of a number and 7

23. 42 divided by a number

24. The quotient of 56 and a number

25. A number multiplied by 12

In Exercises 26–29, use the following information. You belong to a book club. Your yearly book budget is $350. Each book in the book club costs $7.

26. Complete the table.

Books	Cost (dollars)	Amount left (dollars)
1	7	343
2	14	336
3	?	?
4	?	?

27. Write a variable expression for the cost of b books.

28. Write a variable expression for the amount of your budget after b books.

29. How many books will you be able to buy before the $350 is spent?

Name _____ Date _____

Practice C

For use with pages 5-9

Evaluate the expression when z = 5 and k = 1.5.

1. $z - k$ **2.** $k + 1.67$ **3.** kz **4.** $\dfrac{k}{z}$

5. $12.5 - k$ **6.** $z + 32.7$ **7.** $17z$ **8.** $\dfrac{30}{k}$

Evaluate the expression when p = 24, s = 5.5, and t = 2.5.

9. $s + t$ **10.** $s - t$ **11.** $\dfrac{p}{t}$ **12.** ps

13. $3p$ **14.** $\dfrac{120}{p}$ **15.** $p + 23$ **16.** $t - 1.8$

17. Write a variable expression to find the number of centimeters in x meters.

18. Write a variable expression to find the value in dollars of p pennies.

19. Write a variable expression to find the number of seconds in m minutes.

20. Write a variable expression to find the number of quarts in g gallons.

21. A factory produces b bicycles an hour, and runs for h hours a day. Write a variable expression for the number of bicycle tires the factory uses each day. Evaluate the expression when $b = 50$ and $h = 16$.

In Exercises 22–26, use the following information. Your school is organizing a fund-raiser. Each student is asked to sell gift baskets for $15 and candles for $1. The table shows the items sold by 3 students.

Student	Number of Gift Baskets	Number of Candles
Sally	18	63
Steven	13	33
Rose	24	60

22. Write a variable expression for the amount a student received by selling g gift baskets.

23. Find the total amount that each student received for selling gift baskets.

24. Write a variable expression for the total amount a student received by selling g gift baskets and c candles.

25. Find the total amount received by each student.

26. List the students in order from most amount of money received to least amount of money received.

Lesson 1.1

Name _____ Date _____

Study Guide
For use with pages 5-9

GOAL Evaluate and write variable expressions.

VOCABULARY

A **numerical expression** consists of numbers and operations. For example, the expression $10 - 4$ is a numerical expression.

A **variable** is a letter used to represent one or more numbers.

A **variable expression** consists of numbers, variables, and operations. For example, the expression $10 - c$ is a variable expression.

To **evaluate** a variable expression, substitute a number for each variable and evaluate the resulting numerical expression.

A **verbal model** describes a problem using words as labels and using math symbols to relate the words.

EXAMPLE 1 **Evaluating a Variable Expression**

You have $120 in your bank account. You can evaluate the expression $120 + d$ when $d = 28$ to find the amount you have in your bank account after you deposit $28.

Solution

$$120 + d = 120 + 28 \qquad \text{Substitute 28 for } d.$$
$$= 148 \qquad\qquad \text{Add.}$$

Answer: You have $148 in your bank account.

Exercises for Example 1

Evaluate the expression when $m = 9$.

1. $m + 12$ **2.** $5m$ **3.** $24 - m$ **4.** $\dfrac{36}{m}$

5. An average male cheetah travels about 4 miles per day. Evaluate the expression $4 \cdot c$ when $c = 365$ to find about how many miles a cheetah travels in a year.

Name _____ Date _____

Study Guide

For use with pages 5–9

EXAMPLE 2 **Evaluating Expressions with Two Variables**

Evaluate the expression when $a = 6$ and $b = 18$.

a. $b - a = 18 - 6$ Substitute 18 for b and 6 for a.

       $= 12$ Subtract.

b. $\dfrac{b}{a} = \dfrac{18}{6}$ Substitute 18 for b and 6 for a.

      $= 3$ Divide.

Exercises for Example 2

Evaluate the expression when $x = 14$, $y = 7$, and $z = 4$.

6. xz **7.** $z + y$ **8.** $\dfrac{x}{y}$ **9.** $y - z$

EXAMPLE 3 **Writing a Variable Expression**

Grove City, Pennsylvania received 5 fewer inches of rain this year than last year. Use a verbal model to write a variable expression for the number of inches of rain Grove City received this year if you know the number of inches of rain Grove City received last year.

Solution

Let n represent the number of inches of rain Grove City received last year. The word *fewer* indicates subtraction.

    Inches this year = Inches last year − 5

            $= n - 5$

Answer: The number of inches of rain Grove City received this year is $n - 5$.

Exercises for Example 3

Write a variable expression to represent the phrase.

10. The difference of 17 and a number

11. The quotient of a number and 5

12. 10 more than a number

Name _____ Date _____

Challenge Practice

For use with pages 5–9

Evaluate the expression when $x = 3.3$, $y = 2.5$, and $z = 8$.

1. $x + y + z$ **2.** $2zxy$ **3.** $z + x + y - z$

Evaluate the expression when $a = 8.1$, $b = 6$, and $c = 4.7$.

4. $ab + bc$ **5.** $ab - bc$ **6.** $\dfrac{20a}{b}$

Evaluate the expression when $r = 18$, $s = 45$, and $t = 1.4$.

7. $\dfrac{7r}{t}$ **8.** $t(r + s)$ **9.** $t(s - r)$

10. The cost of a rope at a hardware store depends on its length in feet and its
price per foot. Write a variable expression using 4 variables to represent the
cost of 2 ropes that have different lengths and prices per foot. Explain what
each variable represents. Use the expression to evaluate the total cost to buy
a 28-foot rope at $.23 per foot and a 36-foot rope at $.39 per foot.

Teacher's Name _____ Class _____ Room _____ Date _____

Lesson Plan

1-day lesson (See *Pacing and Assignment Guide*, TE page 2A)

For use with pages 10–13

GOAL **Use powers to describe repeated multiplication.**

State/Local Objectives _____

_____

✓ **Check the items you wish to use for this lesson.**

STARTING OPTIONS

_____ Homework Check (1.1): TE page 7; Answer Transparencies

_____ Homework Quiz (1.1): TE page 9; Transparencies

_____ Warm-Up: Transparencies

TEACHING OPTIONS

_____ Notetaking Guide

_____ Examples: 1–3, SE pages 10–11

_____ Extra Examples: TE page 11

_____ Checkpoint Exercises: 1–11, SE pages 10–11

_____ Concept Check: TE page 11

_____ Guided Practice Exercises: 1–12, SE page 12

APPLY/HOMEWORK

Homework Assignment

_____ Basic: SRH p. 789 Exs. 1, 2, 5, 6; pp. 12–13 Exs. 13–33, 36, 39–48

_____ Average: pp. 12–13 Exs. 17–37, 39–49

_____ Advanced: pp. 12–13 Exs. 17–20, 25–29, 32–38*, 43–49

Reteaching the Lesson

_____ Practice: CRB pages 16–18 (Level A, Level B, Level C); Practice Workbook

_____ Study Guide: CRB pages 19–20; Spanish Study Guide

Extending the Lesson

_____ Challenge: SE page 13; CRB page 21

ASSESSMENT OPTIONS

_____ Daily Quiz (1.2): TE page 13 or Transparencies

_____ Standardized Test Practice: SE page 13

Notes

_____

_____

_____

Teacher's Name _____ Class _____ Room _____ Date _____

Lesson Plan for Block Scheduling

Half-block lesson (See *Pacing and Assignment Guide*, TE page 2A)

For use with pages 10–13

GOAL   Use powers to describe repeated multiplication.

State/Local Objectives _____

_____

✓ **Check the items you wish to use for this lesson.**

Chapter Pacing Guide	
Day	**Lesson**
1	1.1; **1.2**
2	1.3; 1.4
3	1.5; 1.6
4	1.7; 1.8
5	Ch. 1 Review and Projects

STARTING OPTIONS

_____ Homework Check (1.1): TE page 7; Answer Transparencies

_____ Homework Quiz (1.1): TE page 9; Transparencies

_____ Warm-Up: Transparencies

TEACHING OPTIONS

_____ Notetaking Guide

_____ Examples: 1–3, SE pages 10–11

_____ Extra Examples: TE page 11

_____ Checkpoint Exercises: 1–11, SE pages 10–11

_____ Concept Check: TE page 11

_____ Guided Practice Exercises: 1–12, SE page 12

APPLY/HOMEWORK

Homework Assignment

_____ Block Schedule: pp. 12–13 Exs. 17–37, 39–49 (with 1.1)

Reteaching the Lesson

_____ Practice: CRB pages 16–18 (Level A, Level B, Level C); Practice Workbook

_____ Study Guide: CRB pages 19–20; Spanish Study Guide

Extending the Lesson

_____ Challenge: SE page 13; CRB page 21

ASSESSMENT OPTIONS

_____ Daily Quiz (1.2): TE page 13 or Transparencies

_____ Standardized Test Practice: SE page 13

Notes _____

_____

_____

_____

Name _____ Date _____

Practice A
For use with pages 10–13

Write the product using an exponent.

1. $16 \cdot 16 \cdot 16$

2. $18 \cdot 18 \cdot 18 \cdot 18 \cdot 18$

3. $(0.4)(0.4)(0.4)(0.4)$

4. $(1.2)(1.2)$

5. $c \cdot c \cdot c \cdot c \cdot c \cdot c \cdot c$

6. $n \cdot n \cdot n \cdot n \cdot n \cdot n \cdot n \cdot n$

Evaluate the expression when $x = 4$ and $y = 0.8$.

7. x^3

8. x^4

9. x^6

10. y^1

11. y^4

12. y^2

Write the power in words and as a repeated multiplication. Then evaluate the power.

13. 19^2

14. 20^3

15. 0.7^3

16. 2.4^2

17. 3.2^3

18. 0.6^4

19. 11^4

20. 9^5

Evaluate the expression when $m = 10$ and $n = 0.12$.

21. m^4

22. m^5

23. m^6

24. n^2

25. n^3

26. n^1

27. Find the area of a square with side length 14 meters.

28. Find the area of a square with side length 2.5 feet.

29. Find the volume of a cube with edge length 2.1 inches.

30. Find the volume of a cube with edge length 6 centimeters.

31. School has been cancelled for the next day due to a snow storm. You call and tell 3 friends the news. Each of your 3 friends calls 3 of their friends. Complete the table. How many calls have been made after stage 8?

Stage	Calls made, as a power	Value of power
1	3^1	3
2	3^2	9
3	?	?
4	?	?
5	?	?

Lesson 1.2

Name _____ Date _____

Practice B

For use with pages 10–13

Write the product using an exponent.

1. $43 \cdot 43 \cdot 43 \cdot 43$

2. $100 \cdot 100 \cdot 100$

3. $x \cdot x \cdot x$

4. $p \cdot p \cdot p \cdot p \cdot p$

Evaluate the expression when $n = 8$ and $n = 0.3$.

5. n^2

6. n^3

7. n^4

8. n^6

9. n^8

10. n^7

Write the power in words and as a repeated multiplication. Then evaluate the power.

11. 9^6

12. 16^4

13. 2.5^4

14. 1.4^3

Evaluate the expression when $x = 0.64$ and $y = 15$.

15. x^3

16. x^2

17. x^1

18. y^3

19. y^4

20. y^5

Find the area of the square.

21.
17 in.

22.
22 ft

23.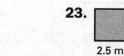
2.5 m

24.
0.6 cm

Find the volume of the cube.

25.
0.9 yd

26.
1.3 ft

27.
30 cm

28.
18 mm

29. Compare each number in the top row of the table with the number below it. Describe any pattern you see. Complete the table with a variable expression involving n.

1	2	3	4	$\cdots$	n
1	16	81	256	$\cdots$	?

Lesson 1.2

Name _____ Date _____

Practice C

For use with pages 10–13

Lesson 1.2

Write the power in words and as a repeated multiplication. Then evaluate the power.

1. 1.4^5 **2.** 2.97^3 **3.** 33^3 **4.** 40^6

Evaluate the expression when $n = 14$ and $n = 0.18$.

5. n^2 **6.** n^1 **7.** n^4

8. n^5 **9.** n^3 **10.** n^6

Find the area of the square figure.

11.
6 in.

12.
8 ft

13.
9 cm

Find the volume of the cubic figure.

14.
15 mm

15.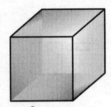
2 cm

16.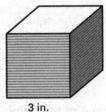
3 in.

Find the value of n.

17. $2^n = 8$ **18.** $4^n = 1024$ **19.** $10^n = 1,000,000$

20. You receive 3 cents for an after school chore. The next day, you receive 9 cents. The third day, you receive 27 cents. Complete the table to find a pattern. How much will you receive after 7 days? Give your answer in dollars.

Day	Amount received, in cents, as a power	Value of the power
1	3^1	3
2	3^2	9
3	3^3	27
4	?	?
5	?	?

Name _____ Date _____

Study Guide
For use with pages 10–13

GOAL Use powers to describe repeated multiplication.

> ## VOCABULARY
>
> A **power** is the result of a repeated multiplication of the same factor. For example, the number 64 is a power because $64 = 4 \cdot 4 \cdot 4$. In the power 4^3, the **base** is 4 and the **exponent** is 3. The *exponent* shows the number of times the *base* is used as a factor.

EXAMPLE 1 **Using Exponents**

Write the product using an exponent.

a. $20 \cdot 20 \cdot 20 \cdot 20 \cdot 20 = 20^5$ — The base 20 is used as a factor 5 times.

b. $(0.6)(0.6)(0.6)(0.6)(0.6)(0.6) = (0.6)^6$ — The base 0.6 is used as a factor 6 times.

c. $m \cdot m \cdot m = m^3$ — The base m is used as a factor 3 times.

Exercises for Example 1

Write the product using an exponent.

1. $21 \cdot 21 \cdot 21$ **2.** $d \cdot d \cdot d \cdot d \cdot d$ **3.** $(2.7)(2.7)(2.7)(2.7)$

Write the power in words and as a repeated multiplication. Then evaluate the power.

4. 2^6 **5.** 7^4 **6.** $(0.4)^3$

EXAMPLE 2 **Evaluating Powers with Variables**

Evaluate the expression y^3 when $y = 0.2$.

Solution

$y^3 = (0.2)^3$ — Substitute 0.2 for y.

$\quad = (0.2)(0.2)(0.2)$ — Use 0.2 as a factor 3 times.

$\quad = 0.008$ — Multiply.

Name _____ Date _____

Study Guide
For use with pages 10–13

Exercises for Example 2

Evaluate the expression when $h = 5$ and when $h = 0.3$.

7. h^2 **8.** h^4 **9.** h^5

EXAMPLE 3 ## Using Powers in Formulas

A florist has a cube-shaped planter in which to plant flowers.
Find the volume of soil needed to fill the planter.

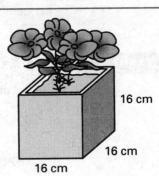

Solution

Use the formula for the volume of a cube.

$V = s^3$ Write the formula.

$\quad = (16)^3$ Substitute 16 for s.

$\quad = 4096$ Evaluate power.

16 cm

16 cm

16 cm

Answer: The volume of soil needed is 4096 cubic centimeters.

Exercises for Example 3

Find the area of a square with the given side length.

10. 4.5 inches   **11.** 13 centimeters

Find the volume of a cube with the given edge length.

12. 8 meters   **13.** 3.4 yards

Name _____ Date _____

Challenge Practice

For use with pages 10–13

Write the product using exponents.

1. $3 \cdot 3 \cdot 3 \cdot 3 \cdot 4 \cdot 4 \cdot 4$

2. $a \cdot a \cdot a \cdot b \cdot b$

Write the product using an exponent.

3. $(x + 2)(x + 2)(x + 2)(x + 2)$

4. $(r + s + t)(r + s + t)$

In Exercises 5–7, evaluate the power when $x = 6$.

5. $(x + 4)^2$

6. $(x - 3)^4$

7. $(8 - x)^8$

8. The product $2 \cdot 2 \cdot 2 \cdot 2 \cdot 2 \cdot 2$ can be written as $(2 \cdot 2 \cdot 2)(2 \cdot 2 \cdot 2)$, which means it can be written as the power 8^2. Find two other ways to write the product $2 \cdot 2 \cdot 2 \cdot 2 \cdot 2 \cdot 2$ as a power.

9. Write the number 1,000,000 as a power in three ways.

10. You are told to draw two squares so that the sum of their areas is 50 square inches and the side length of each square is a whole number of inches. There are two combinations of side lengths for the two squares that will work. Find each possible combination of side lengths.

Teacher's Name _____ Class _____ Room _____ Date _____

Lesson Plan

1-day lesson (See *Pacing and Assignment Guide*, TE page 2A)

For use with pages 16-21

GOAL **Use order of operations to evaluate expressions.**

State/Local Objectives _____

_____

✓ **Check the items you wish to use for this lesson.**

STARTING OPTIONS

_____ Homework Check (1.2): TE page 12; Answer Transparencies

_____ Homework Quiz (1.2): TE page 13; Transparencies

_____ Warm-Up: Transparencies

TEACHING OPTIONS

_____ Notetaking Guide

_____ Examples: 1–4, SE pages 16–18

_____ Extra Examples: TE pages 17–18

_____ Checkpoint Exercises: 1–12, SE page 17

_____ Keystrokes for Technology Activity 1.3 on SE page 21: CRB page 24

_____ Concept Check: TE page 18

_____ Guided Practice Exercises: 1–9, SE page 18

APPLY/HOMEWORK

Homework Assignment

_____ Basic: SRH p. 774 Exs. 1–4, p. 775 Exs. 1–4; pp. 19–20 Exs. 10–35, 40–44

_____ Average: pp. 19–20 Exs. 12–18, 23–38, 40–44

_____ Advanced: pp. 19–20 Exs. 13–18, 23–30, 32–44*

Reteaching the Lesson

_____ Practice: CRB pages 25–27 (Level A, Level B, Level C); Practice Workbook

_____ Study Guide: CRB pages 28–29; Spanish Study Guide

Extending the Lesson

_____ Challenge: SE page 20; CRB page 30

ASSESSMENT OPTIONS

_____ Daily Quiz (1.3): TE page 20 or Transparencies

_____ Standardized Test Practice: SE page 20

Notes

_____

_____

_____

LESSON
1.3
Lesson Plan for Block Scheduling
Half-block lesson (See *Pacing and Assignment Guide*, TE page 2A)

For use with pages 16–21

GOAL **Use order of operations to evaluate expressions.**

State/Local Objectives _____

_____

✓ **Check the items you wish to use for this lesson.**

Chapter Pacing Guide	
Day	Lesson
1	1.1; 1.2
2	**1.3**; 1.4
3	1.5; 1.6
4	1.7; 1.8
5	Ch. 1 Review and Projects

STARTING OPTIONS
_____ Homework Check (1.2): TE page 12; Answer Transparencies

_____ Homework Quiz (1.2): TE page 13; Transparencies

_____ Warm-Up: Transparencies

TEACHING OPTIONS
_____ Notetaking Guide

_____ Examples: 1–4, SE pages 16–18

_____ Extra Examples: TE pages 17–18

_____ Checkpoint Exercises: 1–12, SE page 17

_____ Keystrokes for Technology Activity 1.3 on SE page 21: CRB page 24

_____ Concept Check: TE page 18

_____ Guided Practice Exercises: 1–9, SE page 18

APPLY/HOMEWORK
Homework Assignment

_____ Block Schedule: pp. 19–20 Exs. 12–18, 23–38, 40–44 (with 1.4)

Reteaching the Lesson

_____ Practice: CRB pages 25–27 (Level A, Level B, Level C); Practice Workbook

_____ Study Guide: CRB pages 28–29; Spanish Study Guide

Extending the Lesson

_____ Challenge: SE page 20; CRB page 30

ASSESSMENT OPTIONS
_____ Daily Quiz (1.3): TE page 20 or Transparencies

_____ Standardized Test Practice: SE page 20

Notes _____

_____

_____

_____

Lesson 1.3

Pre-Algebra **23**
Chapter 1 Resource Book

Name _____ Date _____

Technology Activity Keystrokes

For use with Technology Activity 1.3, page 21

TI-34 II

(100 + 87) ÷ (328 + 296) ENTER =

TI-73 Explorer

(100 + 87) ÷ (328 + 296) ENTER

Lesson 1.3

Name _____ Date _____

Practice A

For use with pages 16–21

Evaluate the expression.

1. $3 \cdot 8 + 7$

2. $21 - 4 \cdot 5$

3. $7 \cdot 8 - 19$

4. $2 \cdot 6 + 11 \cdot 1$

5. $4 \cdot 9 - 3 \cdot 2$

6. $16 \div 4 - 24 \div 12$

7. $6 \cdot 5 - 18 \div 3$

8. $90 \div 5 - 3^2$

9. $\dfrac{13 + 11}{14 - 6}$

10. $26 - (4^2 - 8)$

11. $3[5 + (9 - 7)]$

12. $2(12 - 3 \cdot 4)$

13. Find the sum of 17 and 4 squared.

14. Find the difference of 78 and 7 squared.

Evaluate the expression when $x = 4$ and $y = 9$.

15. x^2

16. $6(x - 1)$

17. $7 + y \div 3$

18. $30 - 2y$

19. $3(x + y)^2$

20. $xy \div 3$

21. $y^2 - x$

22. $2xy + 3x$

23. $0.5(y - 5)$

24. $1.4x - 4$

25. $\dfrac{y}{x - 1}$

26. $\dfrac{38 - x - y}{y - x}$

27. You are purchasing supplies for an art project. You need 3 containers of paint, 2 brushes, and 1 case of canvas. Each container of paint is $3.99, each brush is $3.80, and each case of canvas is $15.99. Write and evaluate an expression for the total cost of the art supplies.

28. The formula to find the area A of a rectangle is $A = \ell w$, where ℓ is the length of the rectangle and w is the width of the rectangle. Find the total area of the garden.

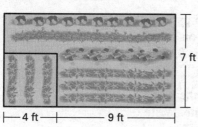

7 ft

4 ft   9 ft

Lesson 1.3

Name _____ Date _____

Evaluate the expression.

1. $6.1(4) + 2(1.5)$

2. $58.4 - 4(9.2)$

3. $\dfrac{2.6 + 3.9}{7.8 - 7.3}$

4. $\dfrac{42 - 17}{0.2(25)}$

5. $7(16 - 2^3)$

6. $9(3 + 5^3)$

7. $2.5[10 + (20 - 2^2)]$

8. $3.1[100 - (5^2 \cdot 3)]$

9. $90 \div [(82 - 77) \cdot 9]$

10. Find the sum of 2 cubed and 3 squared.

11. Find the difference of 10 squared and 9 squared.

Evaluate the expression when $a = 16$, $b = 8$, and $c = 7$.

12. $8c \div 4$

13. $(c + 5) \div 6$

14. $3a + 2.1(4)$

15. $\dfrac{2a}{15 - c}$

16. $7.2b - bc$

17. $b(a - 9.1)$

18. $ac[(99 - b^2) \cdot 2]$

19. $c^3[4.1(3c - 19)]$

20. $\dfrac{b^3(9 - 5.9)}{3.2(20.4 - 12.4)}$

21. The formula to find the area A of a rectangle is $A = \ell w$, where ℓ is the length of the rectangle and w is the width of the rectangle. The figure below can be divided into two rectangles. Find the total area of the figure.

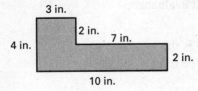

22. You complete a project for your social studies class. There are 3 parts to the project, worth a total of 100 points. You get 50 out of 50 points on part A, and 23 out of 25 points on part C. The total score you received is 93 out of 100. How many points did you get on part B?

23. You use a long distance telephone service that charges $.99 for the first minute of a long distance call and $.10 for each additional minute. Write and evaluate an expression for the total cost of a 17-minute long distance phone call.

Lesson 1.3

Name _____ Date _____

Evaluate the expression.

1. $2.2^2(100 \cdot 5 - 450 \div 9)$

2. $[303 - 1.5^3(22 - 18)] + 47$

3. $\dfrac{17 + 2 \cdot 8}{25 - 14}$

4. $\dfrac{5(3.1 + 1.7)}{81 - 78}$

5. $96 \div [(85 - 79) \cdot 4]$

6. $144 \div [(0.2^3 \cdot 5)(19 + 11)]$

7. $0.8^2[(11.1 - 8.9) + 9^2]$

8. $4^3[1.5^3 + (9.2 - 6.7)]$

9. $3.6^2[(1.7 \cdot 5) + (9.1 \cdot 4)]$

Evaluate the expression when $m = 1.2$, $n = 6$, and $p = 3$.

10. $4m + 3n^2$

11. $8(m^2 + 3n)$

12. $\dfrac{5m + p^2}{p + 2}$

13. $\dfrac{n^3 - 16}{p^2 - 5}$

14. $5(p^3 + 4m)$

15. $9p^2 - 7n$

16. $m + 3[n - (p + 2)]$

17. $(n + p)^2 - 4.3$

18. $p + (n - 1)^3$

19. Find the sum of 1.3 cubed and 0.4 squared.

20. Find the difference of 5 squared and 0.6 cubed.

21. You are bowling for a fund-raiser. You ask friends and family to donate money at a fixed rate per game or an amount per pin knocked down. Eleven people donate $1.25 per game, 5 people donate $.10 per pin, and 3 people donate $.15 per pin. You bowl 4 games and knock down a total of 380 pins. How much money do you raise?

22. The formula to find the area A of a rectangle is $A = \ell w$, where ℓ is the length of the rectangle and w is the width of the rectangle. The figure below can be divided into two rectangles. Find the area of the figure.

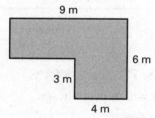

9 m

6 m

3 m

4 m

LESSON
1.3

Study Guide
For use with pages 16–21

GOAL Use order of operations to evaluate expressions.

ORDER OF OPERATIONS

1. Evaluate expressions inside grouping symbols. (Parentheses, brackets, and fraction bars are common grouping symbols.)
2. Evaluate powers.
3. Multiply and divide from left to right.
4. Add and subtract from left to right.

EXAMPLE 1 **Using Grouping Symbols**

Evaluate the expression.

a. $12 \cdot 3 - 18 \div 6 = 36 - 3$ Multiply and divide.
$= 33$ Subtract.

b. $9(10.6 + 7.3) = 9(17.9)$ Add within parentheses.
$= 161.1$ Multiply.

c. $\dfrac{55.4 - 18.5}{2.6 + 0.4} = (55.4 - 18.5) \div (2.6 + 0.4)$ Rewrite fraction as division.
$= 36.9 \div 3$ Evaluate within parentheses.
$= 12.3$ Divide.

EXAMPLE 2 **Evaluating Variable Expressions**

Evaluate the expression $3(x - y)^2$ when $x = 7$ and $y = 3$.

Solution

$3(x - y)^2 = 3(7 - 3)^2$ Substitute 7 for x and 3 for y.
$= 3(4)^2$ Subtract within parentheses.
$= 3(16)$ Evaluate power.
$= 48$ Multiply.

Lesson 1.3

Name _____ Date _____

LESSON
1.3
Continued

Study Guide

For use with pages 16–21

Exercises for Examples 1 and 2

Evaluate the expression.

1. $6 + (25 - 16)^2$

2. $66 \div [(12 + 6) \div 9]$

3. $\dfrac{4(10 - 2)}{3^2 + 7}$

Evaluate the expression when $x = 5$ and $y = 7$.

4. $7(y + x)$

5. $4x - 2y$

6. $\dfrac{2.3x}{y - 2}$

EXAMPLE 3 **Using a Problem Solving Plan**

To start your scrapbook hobby, you bought a scrapbook for $19.99, 2 scissors for $5.50 each, and 3 cropping tools for $8.25 each. Find the total cost.

Solution

Read and Understand You buy several tools and one scrapbook. You are asked to find the total cost.

Make a Plan Write a verbal model.

Total cost	=	Cost of scrapbook	+	Number of scissors	·	Cost of scissors	+	Number of cropping tools	·	Cost of cropping tools

Solve the Problem Write and evaluate an expression.

$$\begin{aligned} \text{Total cost} &= 19.99 + 2 \cdot 5.5 + 3 \cdot 8.25 & &\text{Substitute values into verbal model.} \\ &= 19.99 + 11 + 24.75 & &\text{Multiply.} \\ &= 55.74 & &\text{Add.} \end{aligned}$$

Answer: The total cost is $55.74.

Look Back Use estimation to check that the answer is reasonable.

Exercise for Example 3

7. You buy 3 shirts for $12.99 each and 2 pairs of pants for $24.99 each. Find the total cost.

Lesson 1.3

Challenge Practice

For use with pages 16–21

Evaluate the expression when $x = 7$, $y = x - 4$, and $z = y(x + 13)$.

1. $2yx^2 \div 6x$

2. $\dfrac{xz}{30} + \dfrac{y^3 - 3x}{z \div 10}$

Insert parentheses to make the statement true.

3. $4^2 \times 13 - 9 \div 32 + 4 = 6$

4. $12 - 7 \times 6 + 19 - 14 = 111$

In Exercises 5 and 6, insert an operation symbol for *addition*, *subtraction*, *multiplication*, or *division* in each blank to make the statement true.

5. $90 \underline{} (3 \underline{} 7) \underline{} 3 \underline{} 2 = 15$

6. $4 \underline{} 10^2 \underline{} 1000 \underline{} 5 \underline{} 4 = 204$

7. Emily's school is 800 meters from her house. She walks halfway home when she sees Kerrie behind her. Emily turns around and walks back 80 meters to meet her. The two girls cover one-third of the remaining distance to Emily's house when Dustin yells to them from 60 meters behind. They walk back half that distance to meet him. How far is Emily from her house now? Write and solve an expression to get your answer.

Teacher's Name _____ Class _____ Room _____ Date _____

Lesson Plan

1-day lesson (See *Pacing and Assignment Guide*, TE page 2A)

For use with pages 22–26

GOAL **Compare and order integers.**

State/Local Objectives _____

_____

✓ **Check the items you wish to use for this lesson.**

STARTING OPTIONS

_____ Homework Check (1.3): TE page 19; Answer Transparencies

_____ Homework Quiz (1.3): TE page 20; Transparencies

_____ Warm-Up: Transparencies

TEACHING OPTIONS

_____ Notetaking Guide

_____ Examples: 1–4, SE pages 22–24

_____ Extra Examples: TE pages 23–24

_____ Checkpoint Exercises: 1–9, SE pages 22–24

_____ Concept Check: TE page 24

_____ Guided Practice Exercises: 1–17, SE page 24

APPLY/HOMEWORK

Homework Assignment

_____ Basic: pp. 25–26 Exs. 18–51, 54–56, 66–76

_____ Average: pp. 25–26 Exs. 21–37, 42–53, 57–62, 66–76

_____ Advanced: pp. 25–26 Exs. 21, 24, 25, 30–34, 39, 42–71, 75, 76*

Reteaching the Lesson

_____ Practice: CRB pages 33–35 (Level A, Level B, Level C); Practice Workbook

_____ Study Guide: CRB pages 36–37; Spanish Study Guide

Extending the Lesson

_____ Challenge: SE page 26; CRB page 38

ASSESSMENT OPTIONS

_____ Daily Quiz (1.4): TE page 26 or Transparencies

_____ Standardized Test Practice: SE page 26

_____ Quiz (1.1–1.4): SE page 27; Assessment Book page 7

Notes _____

_____

Teacher's Name _____ Class _____ Room _____ Date _____

Lesson Plan for Block Scheduling

Half-block lesson (See *Pacing and Assignment Guide*, TE page 2A)

For use with pages 22–26

GOAL   **Compare and order integers.**

State/Local Objectives _____

_____

✓ **Check the items you wish to use for this lesson.**

Chapter Pacing Guide	
Day	**Lesson**
1	1.1; 1.2
2	1.3; **1.4**
3	1.5; 1.6
4	1.7; 1.8
5	Ch. 1 Review and Projects

STARTING OPTIONS

_____ Homework Check (1.3): TE page 19; Answer Transparencies

_____ Homework Quiz (1.3): TE page 20; Transparencies

_____ Warm-Up: Transparencies

TEACHING OPTIONS

_____ Notetaking Guide

_____ Examples: 1–4, SE pages 22–24

_____ Extra Examples: TE pages 23–24

_____ Checkpoint Exercises: 1–9, SE pages 22–24

_____ Concept Check: TE page 24

_____ Guided Practice Exercises: 1–17, SE page 24

APPLY/HOMEWORK

Homework Assignment

_____ Block Schedule: pp. 25–26 Exs. 21–37, 42–53, 57–62, 66–76 (with 1.3)

Reteaching the Lesson

_____ Practice: CRB pages 33–35 (Level A, Level B, Level C); Practice Workbook

_____ Study Guide: CRB pages 36–37; Spanish Study Guide

Extending the Lesson

_____ Challenge: SE page 26; CRB page 38

ASSESSMENT OPTIONS

_____ Daily Quiz (1.4): TE page 26 or Transparencies

_____ Standardized Test Practice: SE page 26

_____ Quiz (1.1–1.4): SE page 27; Assessment Book page 7

Notes _____

_____

_____

_____

Lesson 1.4

Name _____ Date _____

Practice A

For use with pages 22–26

Graph the integers on a number line. Then write the integers in order from least to greatest.

1. $-7, 0, 4, -3, -4, 2$ **2.** $8, -2, 7, -1, 9, -3$

3. $6, 9, -5, -7, -3, 2$ **4.** $-5, 0, -1, -7, -6, 1$

Complete the statement using < or >.

5. $-7 \underline{\ ?\ } 4$ **6.** $-5 \underline{\ ?\ } -10$ **7.** $6 \underline{\ ?\ } -3$

8. $9 \underline{\ ?\ } 0$ **9.** $-15 \underline{\ ?\ } -12$ **10.** $-8 \underline{\ ?\ } -2$

State the absolute value of the number.

11. 12 **12.** -17 **13.** -21

14. 32 **15.** 45 **16.** -98

State the opposite of the number.

17. 56 **18.** 37 **19.** -48

20. -65 **21.** 13 **22.** -29

Evaluate the expression when $x = -5$.

23. $-x$ **24.** $|x| + 3$ **25.** $|x| + 7$ **26.** $|-15| - |x|$

27. In miniature golf, *par* is the expected number of strokes to finish a hole. Your score for the game is the sum of your number of strokes above or below par for each hole. The player with the least score wins. Order the scores given in the table from least to greatest to determine the order of finish.

Player	Score
Jerri	-5
Elinor	$+3$
Lance	-2
Hugh	$+1$
Fernando	-3

Name _____ Date _____

Practice B

For use with pages 22–26

Graph the integers on a number line. Then write the integers in order from least to greatest.

1. $-14, -11, -13, -9, -20, -7$

2. $-30, 20, 10, -15, -5, 35$

3. $0, -1, 1, -2, 2, -3, 3$

4. $40, -50, 60, 20, -30, -10$

Complete the statement using < or >.

5. -9 __?__ -17

6. -20 __?__ -12

7. 15 __?__ -18

8. 0 __?__ -24

9. -32 __?__ 21

10. 27 __?__ -14

State the absolute value of the number.

11. -73

12. -80

13. 16

14. 106

15. -34

16. -54

State the opposite of the number.

17. -98

18. -77

19. 45

20. 70

21. 63

22. -23

Evaluate the expression when $x = -7$.

23. $|-x|$

24. $|x| + 4$

25. $2|x|$

26. $6|x|$

27. $|x| - 5$

28. $|x| + 14$

29. $-x - 3$

30. $-x + 10$

31. The table shows the daily low temperatures recorded over a seven-day period in a town.

   a. Did the daily low temperature *increase* or *decrease* from Tuesday to Wednesday?

   b. Did the daily low temperature *increase* or *decrease* from Thursday to Saturday?

   c. Which day's low temperature was lowest? Which was highest?

Day	Temperature
Sunday	$-10°C$
Monday	$-5°C$
Tuesday	$-11°C$
Wednesday	$-10°C$
Thursday	$-6°C$
Friday	$-7°C$
Saturday	$-9°C$

Lesson 1.4

Name _____ Date _____

Practice C

For use with pages 22–26

State the absolute value of the number.

1. -11 **2.** -138 **3.** -43

4. 16 **5.** 151 **6.** 89

State the opposite of the number.

7. 119 **8.** 202 **9.** 97

10. -114 **11.** -213 **12.** -86

Evaluate the expression when $x = -9$ and $y = -15$.

13. $|x| + |y|$ **14.** $(-y) - |x|$ **15.** $-|y|$ **16.** $-|-x|$

17. $-y + |x|$ **18.** $-x + 12$ **19.** $|y| - |x|$ **20.** $|y| - 7$

21. $-(-y)$ **22.** $-x + 20$ **23.** $|y| - 4$ **24.** $|x| + |y| + 11$

25. The table shows the elevation relative to sea level for different places around the world.

   a. Write each elevation relative to sea level as an integer.

   b. Which site is farthest from sea level?

   c. Which site is closest to sea level?

   d. List the sites in order from least elevation relative to sea level to greatest elevation relative to sea level.

Site	Elevation relative to sea level
Mt. McKinley, USA	6194 meters above
Mont Blanc, France-Italy	4807 meters above
Lake Eyre, Australia	12 meters below
Bahia Blanca, South America	42 meters below

Tell whether the equation or inequality is true for *some* values of *a*, for *all* values of *a*, or for *no* values of *a*. If it is true for some values, describe when it is true and when it is false.

26. $|a| > 0$ **27.** $|-a| = |a|$ **28.** $|-a| = -|a|$

Name _____   Date _____

LESSON 1.4 — Study Guide

For use with pages 22–26

GOAL Compare and order integers.

VOCABULARY

The **integers** are the numbers . . ., $-3, -2, -1, 0, 1, 2, 3, \ldots$.
Negative integers are integers that are less than 0. **Positive integers** are integers that are greater than 0.

The **absolute value** of a number is its distance from 0 on a number line.

Two numbers are **opposites** if they have the same absolute value but different signs. For example, -5 and 5 are opposites.

EXAMPLE 1 Graphing and Ordering Integers

Use a number line to order these integers from least to greatest: $3, 0, -6, -2, 1, -5$.

Solution

Graph the integers on a number line.

```
      -6 -5       -2     0  1       3
   ←——•——•——+——+——•——+——•——•——+——•——+——+——+——+——+——→
     -7 -6 -5 -4 -3 -2 -1  0  1  2  3  4  5  6  7  8
```

Read the numbers from left to right: $-6, -5, -2, 0, 1, 3$.

Answer: The integers from least to greatest are: $-6, -5, -2, 0, 1, 3$.

EXAMPLE 2 Finding Absolute Value

State the absolute value of the number.

a. 3   **b.** -4

Solution

a.

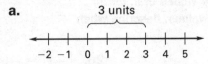

```
        ┌─── 3 units ───┐
   ←——+——+——+——+——+——+——+——+——→
     -2 -1  0  1  2  3  4  5
```

The distance between 3 and 0 is 3. So, $|3| = 3$.

b.

```
        ┌──── 4 units ────┐
   ←——+——+——+——+——+——+——+——+——→
     -5 -4 -3 -2 -1  0  1  2
```

The distance between -4 and 0 is 4. So, $|-4| = 4$.

Lesson 1.4

36   **Pre-Algebra**
Chapter 1   Resource Book

Name _____ Date _____

Study Guide

For use with pages 22–26

EXAMPLE 3 **Finding Opposites**

State the opposite of the number.

a. −8   **b.** 12

Solution

a.

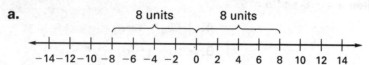

The opposite of −8 is 8.

b.

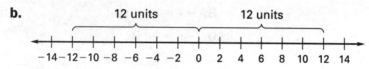

The opposite of 12 is −12.

Exercises for Examples 1–3

Graph the integers on a number line. Then write the integers in order from least to greatest.

1. 16, −4, −9, 5, −1   **2.** 5, −5, 0, −11, 20, 17

State the absolute value of the number. Then state the opposite of the number.

3. −24   **4.** 41   **5.** −63

EXAMPLE 4 **Evaluating Variable Expressions**

Evaluate the expression $|x| - 4$ when $x = -10$.

Solution

$$|x| - 4 = |-10| - 4 \qquad \text{Substitute } -10 \text{ for } x.$$
$$= 10 - 4 \qquad \text{The absolute value of } -10 \text{ is } 10.$$
$$= 6 \qquad \text{Subtract.}$$

Exercises for Example 4

Evaluate the expression when $x = -7$.

6. $9|x|$ **7.** $-7 + (-x)$ **8.** $18 + |x|$

Name _____ Date _____

Challenge Practice

For use with pages 22–26

Order the numbers from least to greatest.

1. $1, -2, -(-3), |-4|, -|5|, -|-6|, -(-|-7|)$

2. $-|22|, -|-17|, 19, -|-(-21)|, 26, -18, -(-17)$

Evaluate the expression when $a = -6$ and $b = 9$.

3. $|-a| + |-b|$

4. $|-b| - (-a)$

5. $|b + (-a)|$

6. $-|b - (-a)|$

Tell whether x is a _positive integer_ or a _negative integer_.

7. $x = -|-x|$

8. $-x = -|-x|$

9. $-x = |-x|$

10. $-x = -|x|$

LESSON

1.5

Teacher's Name _____ Class _____ Room _____ Date _____

Lesson Plan

1-day lesson (See *Pacing and Assignment Guide*, TE page 2A)
For use with pages 28–33

GOAL **Add integers.**

State/Local Objectives _____

_____

✓ Check the items you wish to use for this lesson.

STARTING OPTIONS

_____ Homework Check (1.4): TE page 25; Answer Transparencies

_____ Homework Quiz (1.4): TE page 26; Transparencies

_____ Warm-Up: Transparencies

TEACHING OPTIONS

_____ Notetaking Guide

_____ Concept Activity: SE page 28

_____ Examples: 1–4, SE pages 29–31

_____ Extra Examples: TE pages 30–31

_____ Checkpoint Exercises: 1–9, SE pages 29–31

_____ Concept Check: TE page 31

_____ Guided Practice Exercises: 1–13, SE page 31

APPLY/HOMEWORK

Homework Assignment

_____ Basic: pp. 32–33 Exs. 14–38, 41–44, 47–51, 61–67

_____ Average: pp. 32–33 Exs. 18–23, 27–56, 58, 61–68

_____ Advanced: pp. 32–33 Exs. 21–23, 27–32, 36–66*, 68

Reteaching the Lesson

_____ Practice: CRB pages 41–43 (Level A, Level B, Level C); Practice Workbook

_____ Study Guide: CRB pages 44–45; Spanish Study Guide

Extending the Lesson

_____ Real-World Problem Solving: CRB page 46

_____ Challenge: SE page 33; CRB page 47

ASSESSMENT OPTIONS

_____ Daily Quiz (1.5): TE page 33 or Transparencies

_____ Standardized Test Practice: SE page 33

Notes _____

_____

_____

Teacher's Name _____ Class _____ Room _____ Date _____

LESSON
1.5 Lesson Plan for Block Scheduling

Half-block lesson (See *Pacing and Assignment Guide*, TE page 2A)

For use with pages 28–33

GOAL **Add integers.**

State/Local Objectives _____

_____

✓ **Check the items you wish to use for this lesson.**

Chapter Pacing Guide	
Day	**Lesson**
1	1.1; 1.2
2	1.3; 1.4
3	**1.5**; 1.6
4	1.7; 1.8
5	Ch. 1 Review and Projects

STARTING OPTIONS

_____ Homework Check (1.4): TE page 25; Answer Transparencies

_____ Homework Quiz (1.4): TE page 26; Transparencies

_____ Warm-Up: Transparencies

TEACHING OPTIONS

_____ Notetaking Guide

_____ Concept Activity: SE page 28

_____ Examples: 1–4, SE pages 29–31

_____ Extra Examples: TE pages 30–31

_____ Checkpoint Exercises: 1–9, SE pages 29–31

_____ Concept Check: TE page 31

_____ Guided Practice Exercises: 1–13, SE page 31

APPLY/HOMEWORK

Homework Assignment

_____ Block Schedule: pp. 32–33 Exs. 18–23, 27–56, 58, 61–68 (with 1.6)

Reteaching the Lesson

_____ Practice: CRB pages 41–43 (Level A, Level B, Level C); Practice Workbook

_____ Study Guide: CRB pages 44–45; Spanish Study Guide

Extending the Lesson

_____ Real-World Problem Solving: CRB page 46

_____ Challenge: SE page 33; CRB page 47

ASSESSMENT OPTIONS

_____ Daily Quiz (1.5): TE page 33 or Transparencies

_____ Standardized Test Practice: SE page 33

Notes _____

_____

_____

40 **Pre-Algebra**
Chapter 1 Resource Book

Name _____ Date _____

Practice A

For use with pages 28–33

Tell whether the sum is positive or negative. You do not need to find the sum.

1. $-16 + 43$

2. $-12 + (-9)$

3. $7 + (-32)$

4. $-17 + 13$

Use a number line to find the sum.

5. $-7 + 2$

6. $-8 + 3$

7. $-4 + (-11)$

8. $-5 + (-13)$

9. $6 + (-10)$

10. $15 + (-9)$

11. $-12 + (-1)$

12. $7 + (-14)$

13. $8 + (-6)$

Find the sum.

14. $-21 + (-46)$

15. $-18 + (-53)$

16. $23 + (-40)$

17. $19 + (-17)$

18. $-27 + 35$

19. $-24 + 17$

20. $-33 + 48$

21. $29 + (-13)$

22. $41 + (-37)$

Evaluate the expression when $x = -7$ and $y = 6$.

23. $x + 11$

24. $x + (-20)$

25. $-9 + x$

26. $x + y$

27. $y + (-12)$

28. $-23 + y$

29. You have a checking account. Your balance is $95. You withdraw $32, deposit $80, and withdraw $25. Write an integer to represent each value. Then find the final balance in your account.

30. In consecutive plays, a football team gains 5 yards, loses 3 yards, loses 1 yard, and gains 6 yards. Write an integer to represent each value. What is the net gain for the drive?

LESSON
1.5 **Practice B**

Name _____ Date _____

For use with pages 28–33

Tell whether the sum is positive or negative. You do not need to find the sum.

1. $-27 + (-16)$

2. $-18 + 75$

Use a number line to find the sum.

3. $-15 + (-4)$

4. $-21 + (-5)$

5. $-6 + 35$

6. $-42 + 10$

7. $11 + (-47)$

8. $9 + (-53)$

9. $-106 + (-3)$

10. $-94 + (-1)$

11. $81 + (-7)$

Find the sum.

12. $-41 + 30$

13. $-15 + 27$

14. $-21 + (-34)$

15. $-51 + (-23)$

16. $61 + (-33)$

17. $29 + (-48)$

18. $64 + (-17)$

19. $91 + (-26)$

20. $-46 + (-75)$

21. $-9 + 12 + (-4)$

22. $-22 + (-13) + 6$

23. $55 + (-26) + 47$

Evaluate the expression when $a = 8$ and $b = -14$.

24. $a + (-23)$

25. $-a + b$

26. $-72 + b$

27. $b + 39$

28. $a + (-b)$

29. $-61 + a$

30. The temperature at 6 A.M. is $-10°$ Fahrenheit. During the day, the temperature rises 6°F, drops 3°F, rises 2°F, and drops 8°F. Write an integer to represent each value. What is the temperature after these changes?

31. The table shows incomes and expenses for a small music store in one week. Write an integer to represent each value. Then find the net profit for the week.

Income	Expense
Instruments $800	Displays $110
Sheet music $100	Salaries $400
Lessons $150	

LESSON
1.5

Practice C

For use with pages 28–33

Name _____ Date _____

Use a number line to find the sum.

1. $-50 + 4$ **2.** $-2 + 37$ **3.** $-3 + (-61)$

4. $-71 + (-5)$ **5.** $16 + (-7)$ **6.** $9 + (-21)$

Find the sum.

7. $-83 + (-120)$ **8.** $-55 + 23$ **9.** $41 + (-19)$

10. $-6 + (-11) + (-20)$ **11.** $21 + (-3) + (-24)$ **12.** $-33 + 49 + (-16)$

13. $-51 + (-29) + 70$ **14.** $-31 + (-26) + (-8)$ **15.** $-27 + 62 + (-48)$

16. $-30 + (-46) + 59 + 63$ **17.** $28 + 35 + (-43) + (-60)$

18. $90 + (-12) + 55 + (-37)$ **19.** $-88 + 70 + (-62) + 26$

Evaluate the expression when $m = -25$, $n = -9$, and $p = 18$.

20. $m + n + p$ **21.** $16 + m + (-32)$ **22.** $n + (-11) + (-29)$

23. $(-82) + (-7) + p$ **24.** $p + 23 + n$ **25.** $n + 93 + m$

26. $-24 + m + (-30) + n$ **27.** $n + p + (-33) + 42$

28. $m + n + p + (-m)$ **29.** $n + (-n) + m + p$

30. Tell whether the sum is positive or negative without finding the sum.

    a. $-17 + 8 + (-6)$ **b.** $-2 + 14 + 9$ **c.** $14 + (-5) + (-20)$

31. The table shows 10 transactions on a checking account. The checking account starts with a balance of $100.

    a. Find the balance after each transaction.

    b. What is the final balance?

    c. Does the balance ever become negative? If so, on what transaction?

Transaction	Amount
1	$32 withdrawal
2	$17 withdrawal
3	$20 withdrawal
4	$50 deposit
5	$10 deposit
6	$15 withdrawal
7	$24 withdrawal
8	$29 withdrawal
9	$31 withdrawal
10	$5 withdrawal

Name _____ Date _____

1.5 Study Guide

For use with pages 28–33

GOAL Add integers.

ADDING INTEGERS

1. **Same Sign**   Add the absolute values and use the common sign.
2. **Different Signs**   Subtract the lesser absolute value from the greater absolute value and use the sign of the number with the greater absolute value.
3. **Opposites**   The sum of a number and its opposite is 0. Algebraically, $a + (-a) = 0$ is called the *additive inverse property*.

EXAMPLE 1 Adding Integers Using a Number Line

Use a number line to find the sum.

a. $-2 + (-3)$

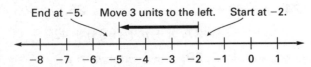

Answer: The final position is -5. So, $-2 + (-3) = -5$.

b. $-6 + 8$

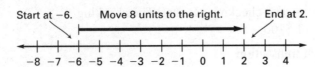

Answer: The final position is 2. So, $-6 + 8 = 2$.

EXAMPLE 2 Adding Two Integers

a. Find the sum $-32 + (-27)$.

Same sign: Add $|-32|$ and $|-27|$.

$$-32 + (-27) = -59$$

Both integers are negative, so the sum is negative.

b. Find the sum $-63 + 39$.

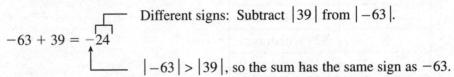

Different signs: Subtract $|39|$ from $|-63|$.

$$-63 + 39 = -24$$

$|-63| > |39|$, so the sum has the same sign as -63.

Name _____ Date _____

Study Guide
For use with pages 28–33

Exercises for Examples 1 and 2

Use a number line to find the sum.

1. $-10 + 7$ **2.** $-3 + (-14)$ **3.** $15 + (-21)$

Find the sum.

4. $45 + (-27)$ **5.** $-31 + (-11)$ **6.** $-89 + 68$

EXAMPLE 3   Adding More Than Two Integers

You record withdrawals and deposits in your checkbook. The starting balance is $265. The first withdrawal is $20. The second withdrawal is $92. The first deposit is $40. What is the final balance?

$$265 + (-20) + (-92) + 40 = 245 + (-92) + 40 \qquad \text{Add 265 and } -20.$$
$$= 153 + 40 \qquad \text{Add 245 and } -92.$$
$$= 193 \qquad \text{Add 153 and 40.}$$

Answer: The sum is 193, so the final balance is $193.

Exercises for Example 3

Find the sum.

7. $-18 + (-33) + 48$ **8.** $75 + (-54) + (-8)$ **9.** $-26 + 41 + (-53)$

EXAMPLE 4   Evaluating Variable Expressions

Evaluate the expression when $a = -18$ and $b = -26$.

a. $34 + a$ **b.** $a + b + 44$

Solution

a. $34 + a = 34 + (-18)$ Substitute -18 for a.
$$= 16 \qquad \text{Add.}$$

b. $a + b + 44 = (-18) + (-26) + 44$ Substitute for a and for b.
$$= -44 + 44 \qquad \text{Add } -18 \text{ and } -26.$$
$$= 0 \qquad \text{Add } -44 \text{ and 44.}$$

Exercises for Example 4

Evaluate the expression when $x = -23$ and $y = -9$.

10. $x + (-8)$ **11.** $14 + y$ **12.** $x + 33 + y$

Name _____ Date _____

Real-World Problem Solving

For use with pages 28–33

Caving

Caving is a sport for people who enjoy maneuvering tight spaces in the dark. It is not an activity for people who are unfit or claustrophobic. Negotiating the inside of a cave may involve walking through large passages, climbing up and down steep inclines, crawling through chambers with low ceilings, and slithering through tunnels so narrow that the human body can barely fit. For safety reasons, caving should never be done alone, without proper equipment and clothing, or without an experienced caver present.

In Exercises 1–3, use the following information.

You and three friends are about to venture deep inside a cave to visit the "rain room" you have heard about. To keep track of how deep you are, you decide to estimate the vertical change you go through at each step along the way. You step through the cave entrance and follow a long, narrow passage that you estimate takes you down about 85 feet. At this point, there is what appears to be a 4-foot drop and the passage turns to the left. You estimate that the passage gradually descends about another 55 feet, then makes a steep drop of about 27 feet into an open chamber. The floor of the chamber seems to rise about 9 feet to the opposite wall where you enter a narrow tunnel with several twists and turns. You estimate that the tunnel takes you down about 22 feet where you enter the rain room. This is a small room about 10 feet in diameter and has about 3 inches of water on the floor. The rain room is named because water drips off of its 5-foot high ceiling to an extent that resembles a heavy rain storm! After you check out the rain room for several minutes, you begin to head back toward the cave entrance.

1. Write an expression that represents your vertical change in altitude from the cave entrance to the rain room as a sum of integers.

2. Evaluate the sum you wrote in Exercise 1.

3. As you emerge from the cave, you meet some cavers who are preparing to enter. They tell you that the rain room is actually 203 feet lower than the entrance to the cave. Add this number to your answer from Exercise 2 to see how close the total of the vertical changes you estimated is to the actual change.

Name _____ Date _____

Challenge Practice

For use with pages 28–33

Find the sum.

 1. $-347 + 67 + (-1243) + 4343 + (-2351)$

 2. $-5760 + 456 + (-992) + (-41) + (-656) + 2208$

In the statement, *a* and *b* are nonzero integers. Explain what must be true about the values of *a* and *b*.

 3. $|a| + b = a + b$

 4. $a + |b| = |a| + b$

 5. $|a + b| \neq |a| + |b|$

 6. $|a + b| = |a| + |b|$

 7. $a + b = 0$

 8. $a + b = 1$

 9. The sum $a + b$ is a negative integer.

 10. The sum $a + (-b)$ is a positive integer.

Teacher's Name _____ Class _____ Room _____ Date _____

Lesson Plan

1-day lesson (See *Pacing and Assignment Guide*, TE page 2A)

For use with pages 34–38

GOAL **Subtract integers.**

State/Local Objectives _____

_____

✓ **Check the items you wish to use for this lesson.**

STARTING OPTIONS

_____ Homework Check (1.5): TE page 32; Answer Transparencies

_____ Homework Quiz (1.5): TE page 33; Transparencies

_____ Warm-Up: Transparencies

TEACHING OPTIONS

_____ Notetaking Guide

_____ Activity Master: CRB page 50

_____ Examples: 1–3, SE pages 34–35

_____ Extra Examples: TE page 35

_____ Checkpoint Exercises: 1–12, SE page 35

_____ Concept Check: TE page 35

_____ Guided Practice Exercises: 1–11, SE page 36

APPLY/HOMEWORK

Homework Assignment

_____ Basic: pp. 36–38 Exs. 12–33, 35–44, 55–66

_____ Average: pp. 36–38 Exs. 18–23, 26–48, 51, 52, 55–66

_____ Advanced: pp. 36–38 Exs. 20–23, 28–55*, 59–66

Reteaching the Lesson

_____ Practice: CRB pages 51–53 (Level A, Level B, Level C); Practice Workbook

_____ Study Guide: CRB pages 54–55; Spanish Study Guide

Extending the Lesson

_____ Challenge: SE page 38; CRB page 56

ASSESSMENT OPTIONS

_____ Daily Quiz (1.6): TE page 38 or Transparencies

_____ Standardized Test Practice: SE page 38

Notes _____

_____

Teacher's Name _____ Class _____ Room _____ Date _____

Lesson Plan for Block Scheduling

Half-block lesson (See *Pacing and Assignment Guide,* TE page 2A)

For use with pages 34–38

GOAL **Subtract integers.**

State/Local Objectives _____

_____

✓ **Check the items you wish to use for this lesson.**

Chapter Pacing Guide	
Day	Lesson
1	1.1; 1.2
2	1.3; 1.4
3	1.5; **1.6**
4	1.7; 1.8
5	Ch. 1 Review and Projects

STARTING OPTIONS

_____ Homework Check (1.5): TE page 32; Answer Transparencies

_____ Homework Quiz (1.5): TE page 33; Transparencies

_____ Warm-Up: Transparencies

TEACHING OPTIONS

_____ Notetaking Guide

_____ Activity Master: CRB page 50

_____ Examples: 1–3, SE pages 34–35

_____ Extra Examples: TE page 35

_____ Checkpoint Exercises: 1–12, SE page 35

_____ Concept Check: TE page 35

_____ Guided Practice Exercises: 1–11, SE page 36

APPLY/HOMEWORK

Homework Assignment

_____ Block schedule: pp. 36–38 Exs. 18–23, 26–48, 51, 52, 55–66 (with 1.5)

Reteaching the Lesson

_____ Practice: CRB pages 51–53 (Level A, Level B, Level C); Practice Workbook

_____ Study Guide: CRB pages 54–55; Spanish Study Guide

Extending the Lesson

_____ Challenge: SE page 38; CRB page 56

ASSESSMENT OPTIONS

_____ Daily Quiz (1.6): TE page 38 or Transparencies

_____ Standardized Test Practice: SE page 38

Notes _____

_____

_____

_____

Name _____ Date _____

Activity Master

For use before Lesson 1.6

Goal	Materials
Subtract integers on a number line.	• pencil and paper

Subtracting Integers on a Number Line

In this activity, you will use a number line to subtract two integers.

INVESTIGATE **Use a number line to find the difference of two integers.**

❶ Subtract $-4 - 6$.

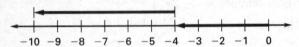

Draw a number line. Place a pencil at 0 and move 4 units to the left to reach -4. Then move 6 units to the left to show the subtraction of 6. Find your final position on the number line.

Copy and complete the statement: $-4 - 6 = \underline{\ ?\ }$.

❷ Subtract $-2 - (-5)$.

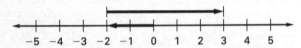

Draw a number line. Place a pencil at 0 and move 2 units to the left to reach -2. Then move 5 units to the right to show the subtraction of -5. Find your final position on the number line.

Copy and complete the statement: $-2 - (-5) = \underline{\ ?\ }$.

DRAW CONCLUSIONS

Use a number line to find the difference.

1. $4 - 8$ **2.** $-1 - (-6)$ **3.** $-7 - 13$

4. $5 - (-6)$ **5.** $2 - 7$ **6.** $-6 - 4$

7. $-9 - 5$ **8.** $1 - 7$ **9.** $-5 - (-12)$

10. $11 - 15$ **11.** $8 - (-9)$ **12.** $6 - 13$

13. Suppose you are subtracting a negative integer from a negative integer. Explain how you can tell without actually subtracting whether the difference of the integers will be *positive*, *negative*, or *zero*. Show an example of each situation.

Name _____ Date _____

Practice A

For use with pages 34–38

Find the difference.

1. $6 - 9$
2. $11 - 15$
3. $3 - (-7)$
4. $5 - (-12)$
5. $-8 - 4$
6. $-13 - 2$
7. $-1 - (-10)$
8. $-7 - (-5)$
9. $-14 - (-3)$

Evaluate the expression when $m = -5$ and $n = -7$.

10. $m - 9$
11. $-8 - m$
12. $n - 6$
13. $m - n$
14. $n - 11$
15. $12 - m$

Find the change in temperature or elevation.

16. From $-14°C$ to $5°C$
17. From $-21°C$ to $-3°C$
18. From $-7°F$ to $16°F$
19. From $-12°F$ to $32°F$
20. From -80 feet to -45 feet
21. From -37 yards to 15 yards
22. From 24 meters to -8 meters
23. From -13 meters to -21 meters

24. Find the value of the expression $-6 - (-12) - 4$.

25. Find the value of the expression $9 - 16 - (-8)$.

26. In one day, the temperature rose from $-9°F$ to $15°F$. Find the temperature change.

27. An airplane moves from its cruising altitude of 36,000 feet to an altitude of 29,875 feet. What is the change in altitude?

28. At 6 A.M., the outside temperature is $32°F$. Starting at 8 A.M., you record the temperature every 2 hours. At the first recording, the temperature drops $3°F$, at the second recording, the temperature drops an additional $5°F$. At the third and final recording, the temperature drops an additional $2°F$. What is the temperature after the final recording?

Name _____ Date _____

Practice B

For use with pages 34–38

Find the difference.

1. $7 - 11$ **2.** $15 - 26$ **3.** $4 - (-20)$

4. $13 - (-8)$ **5.** $-12 - 9$ **6.** $-19 - 28$

7. $-2 - (-24)$ **8.** $-18 - (-5)$ **9.** $-21 - (-6)$

Evaluate the expression when $x = -14$ and $y = -3$.

10. $x - y$ **11.** $29 - x$ **12.** $x - (-17)$

13. $-27 - y$ **14.** $y - 18$ **15.** $x - (-23)$

16. $x - 4 - 9$ **17.** $15 - y - 7$ **18.** $31 - 35 - y$

Find the change in temperature or elevation.

19. From $-16°C$ to $23°C$ **20.** From $-47°C$ to $-38°C$

21. From $9°F$ to $-12°F$ **22.** From $-16°F$ to $-27°F$

23. From -64 meters to -40 meters   **24.** From -20 meters to 50 meters

25. From 120 yards to -45 yards   **26.** From -16 feet to -32 feet

27. Find the value of the expression $-9 - (-4) - 6$.

28. Find the value of the expression $102 - (-7) - 270$.

29. A group of hikers on a mountain began at an elevation of 3040 feet above sea level and stopped at an elevation of 2319 feet above sea level. What was their change in elevation between these points? How can you tell from the change in elevation whether the hikers were going up or down the mountain?

30. The temperature at 6 A.M. was 63°F. At 3 P.M., the temperature was 41°F. What was the change in temperature?

Name _____ Date _____

Practice C

For use with pages 34–38

Find the difference.

1. 24 − 19

2. 33 − 47

3. 51 − (−27)

4. 42 − (−21)

5. −36 − 26

6. −45 − 70

7. −54 − (−17)

8. −63 − (−88)

9. −100 − (−81)

Evaluate the expression when $a = -53$, $b = 20$ and $c = -9$.

10. $a - c$

11. $b - c$

12. $b - (-33) - c$

13. $-15 - b - a$

14. $a - b - c$

15. $c - b - a$

Find the change in temperature or elevation.

16. From 15°C to −36°C

17. From −10°F to −78°F

18. From −8 meters to −24 meters

19. From 5 feet to −120 feet

Find the value of the expression.

20. −24 − (−11) − 30

21. −110 − 98 − 213

22. −75 − 68 − (−81)

23. 100 − (−93) − (−77)

Evaluate the expression $8 - (-x) + 9 - 15$ for the given value of x.

24. 23

25. 7

26. −6

27. −12

28. A company lost $65,000 during the first 6 months of the year. By the end of the year, the company had an overall profit of $36,200. What was the profit during the second half of the year?

29. A company's quarterly profits are shown in the bar graph.

   a. What is the difference between the first quarter profits and the second quarter profits?

   b. What is the difference between the second quarter profits and the third quarter profits?

   c. What is the difference between the third quarter profits and the fourth quarter profits?

   d. What is the difference between the first quarter profits and the fourth quarter profits?

   e. What is the company's profit for the year?

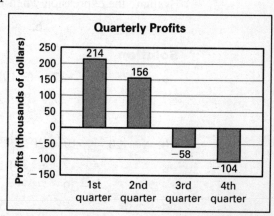

LESSON 1.6

Study Guide

For use with pages 34–38

Lesson 1.6

GOAL Subtract integers.

SUBTRACTING INTEGERS

Words   To subtract an integer, add its opposite.

Numbers $4 - 8 = 4 + (-8) = -4$

Algebra $a - b = a + (-b)$

EXAMPLE 1 Subtracting Integers

a. $9 - 20 = 9 + (-20)$ To subtract 20, add its opposite, -20.

         $= -11$ Add 9 and -20.

b. $10 - (-3) = 10 + 3$ To subtract -3, add its opposite, 3.

         $= 13$ Add 10 and 3.

c. $-6 - (-4) = -6 + 4$ To subtract -4, add its opposite, 4.

         $= -2$ Add -6 and 4.

Exercises for Example 1

Find the difference.

1. $7 - 16$ **2.** $-8 - 5$ **3.** $9 - (-11)$ **4.** $-1 - (-9)$

EXAMPLE 2 Evaluating Variable Expressions

Evaluate the expression when $y = -19$.

a. $-37 - y$ **b.** $y - 20$

Solution

a. $-37 - y = -37 - (-19)$ Substitute -19 for y.

            $= -37 + 19$ To subtract -19, add 19.

            $= -18$ Add -37 and 19.

b. $y - 20 = -19 - 20$ Substitute -19 for y.

           $= -19 + (-20)$ To subtract 20, add -20.

           $= -39$ Add -19 and -20.

Name _____ Date _____

Study Guide

For use with pages 34–38

Exercises for Example 2

Evaluate the expression when $m = -8$.

5. $15 - m$ **6.** $-23 - m$ **7.** $m - 3$ **8.** $30 - m - 13$

EXAMPLE 3 Evaluating Change

Mount Whitney in California has an elevation of 14,494 feet above sea level. Death Valley in California has an elevation of 282 feet below sea level. What is the difference between these elevations?

Solution

Difference in elevation	=	Elevation of Mt. Whitney	−	Elevation of Death Valley

$= 14,494 - (-282)$ Substitute values.

$= 14,494 + 282$ To subtract -282, add 282.

$= 14,776$ Add 14,494 and 282.

Answer: The difference between the elevations is 14,776 feet.

Exercises for Example 3

Find the change in temperature or elevation.

9. From $-26°C$ to $13°C$ **10.** From $-4°F$ to $-16°F$

11. From -140 feet to -57 feet **12.** From 33 meters to -71 meters

Name _____ **Date** _____

Challenge Practice

For use with pages 34–38

Evaluate the expression when $r = -13$, $s = -52$, and $t = 29$.

1. $s + t - r + 5$

2. $-45 + r - t - s$

3. $s - (r - t - 14)$

4. $s - (r + 23 - t)$

In Exercises 5–8, the variables a and b are integers. Tell whether the value of the expression is *positive*, *negative*, or *could be either* under the given conditions.

5. $b - a$ given that $b < a$

6. $|b| - a$ given that $b > a$

7. $|b| - a$ given that $b < a$

8. $|b| - |a|$ given that $b > a$

9. The table below shows the changes this month in a money market account fund. Round the amounts in the right column to dollars and write an expression to approximate the new account balance. Amounts in parentheses should be subtracted from the beginning balance and amounts not in parentheses should be added.

RECONCILIATION OF ACCOUNT BALANCES	
• BEGINNING BALANCE	76,112.10
• TRANSFERS OUT OF ACCOUNT	(227.34)
• OUTSTANDING CHECKS	(33.78)
• TRANSFERS INTO ACCOUNT	0.00
• DEPOSITS IN TRANSIT	0.00
• NEW CHECKS	(1373.06)
• BANK CHARGES	(5.00)
• INTEREST	325.13

Teacher's Name _____ Class _____ Room _____ Date _____

Lesson Plan

1-day lesson (See *Pacing and Assignment Guide*, TE page 2A)
For use with pages 41–46

GOAL   **Multiply and divide integers.**

State/Local Objectives _____

_____

_____

✓ Check the items you wish to use for this lesson.

STARTING OPTIONS

_____ Homework Check (1.6): TE page 36; Answer Transparencies

_____ Homework Quiz (1.6): TE page 38; Transparencies

_____ Warm-Up: Transparencies

TEACHING OPTIONS

_____ Notetaking Guide

_____ Concept Activity: SE page 41

_____ Examples: 1–4, SE pages 42–44

_____ Extra Examples: TE pages 43–44

_____ Checkpoint Exercises: 1–8, SE page 43

_____ Concept Check: TE page 44

_____ Guided Practice Exercises: 1–11, SE page 44

APPLY/HOMEWORK

Homework Assignment

_____ Basic: SRH p. 781 Exs. 1–3; pp. 45–46 Exs. 12–25, 27–39, 45–51

_____ Average: pp. 45–46 Exs. 18–41, 45–52

_____ Advanced: pp. 45–46 Exs. 20–28, 33–52*

Reteaching the Lesson

_____ Practice: CRB pages 59–61 (Level A, Level B, Level C); Practice Workbook

_____ Study Guide: CRB pages 62–63; Spanish Study Guide

Extending the Lesson

_____ Challenge: SE page 46; CRB page 64

ASSESSMENT OPTIONS

_____ Daily Quiz (1.7): TE page 46 or Transparencies

_____ Standardized Test Practice: SE page 46

Notes _____

_____

_____

Teacher's Name _____ Class _____ Room _____ Date _____

Lesson Plan for Block Scheduling

Half-block lesson (See *Pacing and Assignment Guide*, TE page 2A)

For use with pages 41–46

GOAL **Multiply and divide integers.**

State/Local Objectives _____

_____

✓ **Check the items you wish to use for this lesson.**

Chapter Pacing Guide	
Day	**Lesson**
1	1.1; 1.2
2	1.3; 1.4
3	1.5; 1.6
4	**1.7**; 1.8
5	Ch. 1 Review and Projects

STARTING OPTIONS

_____ Homework Check (1.6): TE page 36; Answer Transparencies

_____ Homework Quiz (1.6): TE page 38; Transparencies

_____ Warm-Up: Transparencies

TEACHING OPTIONS

_____ Notetaking Guide

_____ Concept Activity: SE page 41

_____ Examples: 1–4, SE pages 42–44

_____ Extra Examples: TE pages 43–44

_____ Checkpoint Exercises: 1–8, SE page 43

_____ Concept Check: TE page 44

_____ Guided Practice Exercises: 1–11, SE page 44

APPLY/HOMEWORK

Homework Assignment

_____ Block Schedule: pp. 45–46 Exs. 18–41, 45–52 (with 1.8)

Reteaching the Lesson

_____ Practice: CRB pages 59–61 (Level A, Level B, Level C); Practice Workbook

_____ Study Guide: CRB pages 62–63; Spanish Study Guide

Extending the Lesson

_____ Challenge: SE page 46; CRB page 64

ASSESSMENT OPTIONS

_____ Daily Quiz (1.7): TE page 46 or Transparencies

_____ Standardized Test Practice: SE page 46

Notes _____

_____

_____

Name _____ Date _____

Practice A

For use with pages 41–46

Tell whether the product or quotient is *positive* or *negative*. You do not need to find the product or quotient.

1. $-26(3)$

2. $-9(-12)$

3. $20(-11)$

4. $\dfrac{437}{-19}$

5. $\dfrac{-448}{-32}$

6. $-357 \div 21$

Find the product or quotient.

7. $-8(-13)$

8. $-10(17)$

9. $0(-59)$

10. $6(-15)$

11. $-12(5)$

12. $-9(-14)$

13. $75 \div (-3)$

14. $0 \div (-47)$

15. $39 \div (-13)$

16. $\dfrac{-126}{-9}$

17. $\dfrac{-84}{21}$

18. $\dfrac{120}{-24}$

Simplify.

19. $9(-11)(-4)$

20. $-8(-12)(-3)$

21. $14(-20)(-7)$

22. $120 \div (-4) \div (-5)$

23. $-240 \div (-16) \div 5$

24. $90 \div (-3) \div 3$

25. $-3(18) \div 6$

26. $-20(-15) \div 5$

27. $10(27) \div (-15)$

28. The table shows a town's average daily temperature each month for 1 year. Find the mean average daily temperature.

Month	Jan	Feb	Mar	Apr	May	Jun
Temperature	$-15°$F	$-9°$F	$21°$F	$44°$F	$54°$F	$67°$F

Month	Jul	Aug	Sep	Oct	Nov	Dec
Temperature	$71°$F	$71°$F	$63°$F	$58°$F	$34°$F	$21°$F

29. You have 25 shares of stock A, 10 shares of stock B, and 5 shares of stock C. In one day, the price per share changed by $6 for stock A, $-$7 for stock B, and $-$9 for stock C. Find the total change in value of your stock.

Name _____ Date _____

Practice B

For use with pages 41–46

Tell whether the product or quotient is *positive* or *negative*. You do not need to find the product or quotient.

1. $16(-23)$

2. $\dfrac{-72}{9}$

3. $-26(-17) \div 13$

Find the product or quotient.

4. $25(-5)$

5. $-29(-4)$

6. $-124 \div 31$

7. $98 \div (-14)$

8. $\dfrac{-102}{-17}$

9. $-32(9)$

10. $-42(-6)$

11. $201 \div (-67)$

12. $-612 \div (-18)$

13. $\dfrac{252}{-4}$

14. $-19(7)$

15. $-21(-11)$

Simplify.

16. $-15(16)(4)$

17. $20(-13)(-32)$

18. $-220 \div 11 \div (-4)$

19. $140 \div (-7) \div (-5)$

20. $24(-8) \div (-6)$

21. $\dfrac{-9(27)}{3}$

Without performing the indicated divisions, complete the statement using >, <, or =.

22. $-642 \div 214$ __?__ $-170 \div (-10)$

23. $-344 \div (-86)$ __?__ $-796 \div 199$

24. Evaluate the expression $\dfrac{5y}{6}$ when $y = 18$.

25. Evaluate the expression $\dfrac{-2m}{9}$ when $m = 27$.

26. The table shows the lowest windchill temperature for each day recorded over two weeks. Find the mean lowest windchill temperature.

Day	Windchill (in °C)	Day	Windchill (in °C)
1	−4	8	−4
2	−5	9	−6
3	−7	10	−2
4	−3	11	−4
5	−3	12	−6
6	−6	13	−10
7	−1	14	−9

Lesson 1.7

Practice C

For use with pages 41–46

Find the product or quotient.

1. $72 \div (-9)$
2. $-108 \div (-36)$
3. $-25(-7)$
4. $33(-12)$
5. $-91(16)$
6. $-88(-6)$
7. $\dfrac{-315}{45}$
8. $\dfrac{1125}{-15}$
9. $\dfrac{742}{-14}$
10. $-754 \div 29$
11. $71(-62)$
12. $-59(21)$

Simplify.

13. $-41(-11)(5)$
14. $36(-15)(8)$
15. $2576 \div (-56) \div (-23)$
16. $-3072 \div (-48) \div (-8)$
17. $\dfrac{24(-15)}{12}$
18. $\dfrac{-1200}{-48(5)}$

Evaluate the variable expression when $x = 12$.

19. $-8x(-7)$
20. $-9x^2$
21. $-3x^2(10)$
22. $\dfrac{-108}{x}$
23. $x^2 \div (-4)$
24. $-5x \div 15$

Evaluate the expression.

25. $-\dfrac{3}{4}[-6 \cdot (14 \cdot 4) + 16] \div 40$
26. $\left[\left(5\dfrac{1}{2} \cdot 3\right) \div 1\dfrac{1}{2}\right] + \left[\left(6\dfrac{1}{2} \cdot 16\right) \div 13\right]$

27. A golf ball's height, in feet, above the ground t seconds after it is hit is given by the equation $h = -16t^2 + 214t$. Find the height of the ball 3 seconds after it is hit.

28. The table shows yards gained or lost by a football team for 10 plays. Find the mean yards gained or lost. Then find the median yards gained or lost. Does the mean or the median represent a lower number of yards gained or lost?

Play	1	2	3	4	5	6	7	8	9	10
Yards Gained or Lost	gained 14 yd	lost 9 yd	gained 8 yd	gained 7 yd	gained 5 yd	lost 10 yd	lost 2 yd	gained 2 yd	gained 8 yd	lost 3 yd

LESSON

1.7 **Study Guide**

For use with pages 41–46

GOAL **Multiply and divide integers.**

MULTIPLYING AND DIVIDING INTEGERS

The product (or quotient) of two integers with the *same* sign is *positive*.

The product (or quotient) of two integers with *different* signs is *negative*.

The product of any integer and 0 is 0.

The quotient of 0 and any nonzero integer is 0.

EXAMPLE 1 **Multiplying Integers**

    a. $-5(-10) = 50$ Same sign: Product is positive.

    b. $-9(9) = -81$ Different signs: Product is negative.

    c. $-18(0) = 0$ The product of any integer and 0 is 0.

EXAMPLE 2 **Multiplying Integers**

Your uncle owns 90 shares of stock A and 130 shares of stock B. In one day, the price per share changed by +$3 for stock A and −$2 for stock B. Find the total change in value of your uncle's stock.

Solution

$$\boxed{\begin{array}{c}\text{Total}\\\text{change}\end{array}} = \boxed{\begin{array}{c}\text{Stock A}\\\text{shares}\end{array}} \cdot \boxed{\begin{array}{c}\text{Change in}\\\text{1 share}\end{array}} + \boxed{\begin{array}{c}\text{Stock B}\\\text{shares}\end{array}} \cdot \boxed{\begin{array}{c}\text{Change in}\\\text{1 share}\end{array}}$$

    $= 90(3) + 130(-2)$ Substitute values.

    $= 270 + (-260)$ Multiply.

    $= 10$ Add.

Answer: The total change in value was 10. The value of the stocks increased by $10.

EXAMPLE 3 **Dividing Integers**

    a. $-63 \div (-9) = 7$ Same sign: Quotient is positive.

    b. $144 \div (-12) = -12$ Different signs: Quotient is negative.

    c. $0 \div (-8) = 0$ The quotient of 0 and any nonzero integer is 0.

Lesson 1.7

Name _____ Date _____

Study Guide
For use with pages 41–46

Exercises for Examples 1–3

Find the product or quotient.

1. $18(3)$

2. $78 \div (-6)$

3. $-66 \div (-22)$

4. $-8(-11)$

5. $\dfrac{-240}{12}$

6. $9(-15)$

7. A deep sea diver is at a depth of 9 feet below sea level. The diver's depth is changing by -5 feet per second. What is the diver's position after 15 seconds?

EXAMPLE 4 ## Finding a Mean

The table shows the daily minimum temperature in Nome, Alaska for 7 consecutive days in December. Find the mean of the temperatures.

Day	T	W	Th	F	S	S	M
Low temperature (°F)	3	1	−2	−6	−11	−7	−20

Solution

To find the mean of the temperatures, first add the temperatures. Then divide by 7, the number of temperatures.

$$\text{Mean} = \frac{3 + 1 + (-2) + (-6) + (-11) + (-7) + (-20)}{7}$$

$$= \frac{-42}{7}$$

$$= -6$$

Answer: The mean of the temperatures is $-6°F$.

Exercises for Example 4

Find the mean of the data.

8. $-15, 5, -22, -4, -9, -37, 11, -9$

9. $-64, -23, -17, 10, -36, -8, 42, -79, 13$

LESSON
1.7 Challenge Practice

For use with pages 41–46

Evaluate the expression.

1. $-4(-7)(2)(-3) \div (-8)$

2. $-5(4)(-3)(2)(-1) \div (-15)$

3. $\dfrac{-7(-9)(-12)}{3(-18)}$

4. $\dfrac{45(-3)(-4)}{-15(6)}$

5. $\dfrac{(-3)^7(-2)^6}{(-3)^6(-2)^5}$

6. $\dfrac{(-7)^{11}(13)^4}{(-7)^9(-13)^4}$

In Exercises 7–10, use the following information. A company makes a product that it sells for $20 per unit. The materials to produce each unit of the product cost $8. Each day the product is produced, there are fixed setup and cleanup costs totaling $2000. So, the net profit P for producing x units per day is given by the equation $P = 20x + (-8x) - 2000$.

7. Find the net profit for producing 400 units of the product in one day.

8. Find the net profit for producing 200 units of the product each day for 4 consecutive days.

9. Find the net profit for producing 120 units of the product in one day. What does it mean to have a negative profit?

10. Find the net profit for producing 165 units of the product each day for 4 consecutive days.

Lesson 1.7

Teacher's Name _____ Class _____ Room _____ Date _____

Lesson Plan

1-day lesson (See *Pacing and Assignment Guide,* TE page 2A)
For use with pages 47–51

GOAL **Identify and plot points in a coordinate plane.**

State/Local Objectives _____

_____

✓ **Check the items you wish to use for this lesson.**

STARTING OPTIONS

_____ Homework Check (1.7): TE page 45; Answer Transparencies
_____ Homework Quiz (1.7): TE page 46; Transparencies
_____ Warm-Up: Transparencies

TEACHING OPTIONS

_____ Notetaking Guide
_____ Examples: 1–3, SE pages 47–48
_____ Extra Examples: TE page 48
_____ Checkpoint Exercises: 1–7, SE pages 47–48
_____ Concept Check: TE page 48
_____ Guided Practice Exercises: 1–7, SE page 49

APPLY/HOMEWORK

Homework Assignment
_____ Basic: pp. 49–51 Exs. 8–24, 27–29, 35–44
_____ Average: pp. 49–51 Exs. 12–31, 35–44
_____ Advanced: pp. 49–51 Exs. 14–16, 21–44*

Reteaching the Lesson
_____ Practice: CRB pages 67–69 (Level A, Level B, Level C); Practice Workbook
_____ Study Guide: CRB pages 70–71; Spanish Study Guide

Extending the Lesson
_____ Real-World Problem Solving: CRB page 72
_____ Challenge: SE page 51; CRB page 73

ASSESSMENT OPTIONS

_____ Daily Quiz (1.8): TE page 51 or Transparencies
_____ Standardized Test Practice: SE page 51
_____ Quiz (1.5–1.8): Assessment Book page 8

Notes _____

_____

Teacher's Name _____ Class _____ Room _____ Date _____

Lesson Plan for Block Scheduling

Half-block lesson (See *Pacing and Assignment Guide*, TE page 2A)

For use with pages 47–51

GOAL   **Identify and plot points in a coordinate plane.**

State/Local Objectives _____

_____

✓ **Check the items you wish to use for this lesson.**

Chapter Pacing Guide	
Day	**Lesson**
1	1.1; 1.2
2	1.3; 1.4
3	1.5; 1.6
4	1.7; **1.8**
5	Ch. 1 Review and Projects

STARTING OPTIONS

_____   Homework Check (1.7): TE page 45; Answer Transparencies

_____   Homework Quiz (1.7): TE page 46; Transparencies

_____   Warm-Up: Transparencies

TEACHING OPTIONS

_____   Notetaking Guide

_____   Examples: 1–3, SE pages 47–48

_____   Extra Examples: TE page 48

_____   Checkpoint Exercises: 1–7, SE pages 47–48

_____   Concept Check: TE page 48

_____   Guided Practice Exercises: 1–7, SE page 49

APPLY/HOMEWORK

Homework Assignment

_____   Block Schedule: pp. 49–51 Exs. 12–31, 35–44 (with 1.7)

Reteaching the Lesson

_____   Practice: CRB pages 67–69 (Level A, Level B, Level C); Practice Workbook

_____   Study Guide: CRB pages 70–71; Spanish Study Guide

Extending the Lesson

_____   Real-World Problem Solving: CRB page 72

_____   Challenge: SE page 51; CRB page 73

ASSESSMENT OPTIONS

_____   Daily Quiz (1.8): TE page 51 or Transparencies

_____   Standardized Test Practice: SE page 51

_____   Quiz (1.5–1.8): Assessment Book page 8

Notes _____

_____

_____

Lesson 1.8

Name _____   Date _____

Practice A

For use with pages 47–51

Give the coordinates of the point.

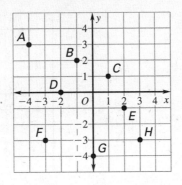

1. A   **2.** B

3. C   **4.** D

5. E   **6.** F

7. G   **8.** H

Plot the point in a coordinate plane. Describe the location of the point.

9. $(-3, -4)$ **10.** $(1, -4)$ **11.** $(5, -2)$

12. $(-6, 0)$ **13.** $(4, -7)$ **14.** $(3, -5)$

15. $(-1, 4)$ **16.** $(-2, 3)$ **17.** $(-3, -5)$

18. Use a coordinate plane.

    a. Plot the points $(-3, -1)$, $(3, -1)$, $(3, 5)$, and $(-3, 5)$. Connect the points in order. Connect the last point to the first point.

    b. Identify the figure. Explain your reasoning.

19. The table shows the attendance at a school's talent show from 1999 to 2004.

Year	1999	2000	2001	2002	2003	2004
Number of attendees	1564	1601	1589	1623	1635	1650

    a. Make a scatter plot of the data.

    b. Describe any relationship you see.

20. The table shows the number of hours students spent studying for an exam and the score, as a percent, received on the exam.

Time spent studying (hours)	1	2	3	4	5	6	7
Exam score (percent)	58	60	72	85	91	96	94

    a. Make a scatter plot of the data.

    b. Describe any relationship you see.

Name _____ Date _____

Practice B

For use with pages 47–51

Give the coordinates of the point.

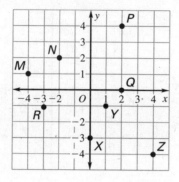

1. X **2.** Y

3. Z **4.** M

5. N **6.** P

7. Q **8.** R

Plot the point in a coordinate plane. Describe the location of the point.

9. $(-7, 6)$ **10.** $(-5, -3)$ **11.** $(2, 3)$

12. $(5, 2)$ **13.** $(-4, 0)$ **14.** $(3, -6)$

15. $(-2, 1)$ **16.** $(5, 0)$ **17.** $(0, -2)$

18. Use a coordinate plane.

   a. Plot the points $(0, 0)$, $(0, 4)$, $(5, 4)$, $(8, 2)$, and $(5, 0)$. Connect the points in order. Connect the last point to the first point.

   b. Identify the figure. Explain your reasoning.

19. Use the variable expression $3x - 1$.

   a. Evaluate the expression when $x = -3, -2, -1, 0, 1, 2,$ and 3.

   b. Use your results from part (a) to write a list of ordered pairs in the form $(x, 3x - 1)$.

   c. Plot the ordered pairs $(x, 3x - 1)$ from part (b) in a coordinate plane.

   d. Describe what you notice about the points.

20. The table shows the number of women who finished the New York City Marathon from 1997 to 2001.

Year	1997	1998	1999	2000	2001
Women Finishers	8413	8332	9160	8332	6853

   a. Make a scatter plot of the data.

   b. Describe any relationship you see.

Lesson 1.8

Name _____ Date _____

Practice C

For use with pages 47–51

Give the coordinates of the point.

1. *A*   2. *B*

3. *C*   4. *D*

5. *E*   6. *F*

7. *G*   8. *H*

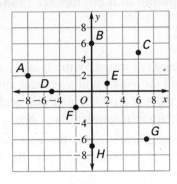

Plot the point in a coordinate plane. Describe the location of the point.

9. $(-10, -11)$ 10. $(9, 8)$ 11. $(6, 12)$

12. $(-7, 9)$ 13. $(4, -6)$ 14. $(8, -16)$

15. Use a coordinate plane.

    a. Plot the points $(-6, 0)$, $(-3, 2)$, $(1, 2)$, $(4, 0)$, $(4, -4)$, $(1, -6)$, $(-3, -6)$, and $(-6, -4)$. Connect the points in order. Connect the last point to the first point.

    b. Identify the figure. Explain your reasoning.

16. Use the variable expression $5 - 2x$.

    a. Evaluate the expression when $x = -3, -2, -1, 0, 1, 2,$ and 3.

    b. Use your results from part (a) to write a list of ordered pairs in the form $(x, 5 - 2x)$.

    c. Plot the ordered pairs $(x, 5 - 2x)$ from part (b) in a coordinate plane.

    d. Describe what you notice about the points.

17. The table shows the average length in centimeters and the average weight in kilograms of 5 types of sharks.

Species	Dusky Shark	Silky Shark	Sandbar Shark	Night Shark	Tiger Shark
Length (cm)	162	118	129	111	203
Weight (kg)	69	22	30	15	110

    a. Make a scatter plot of the data.

    b. Describe any relationship you see.

Name _____   Date _____

Study Guide

For use with pages 47–51

GOAL   Identify and plot points in a coordinate plane.

VOCABULARY

A **coordinate plane** is formed by the intersection of a horizontal number line called the **x-axis** and a vertical number line called the **y-axis.** The axes meet at a point called the **origin** and divide the coordinate plane into four **quadrants.**

Each point in a coordinate plane is represented by an **ordered pair.** The first number is the **x-coordinate,** and the second number is the **y-coordinate.**

A **scatter plot** uses a coordinate plane to display paired data.

EXAMPLE 1   **Naming Points in a Coordinate Plane**

Give the coordinates of the point.

a. *A*   **b.** *B*

Solution

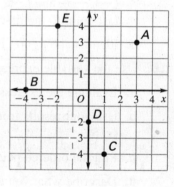

a. Point *A* is 3 units to the right of the origin and 3 units up. The *x*-coordinate is 3 and the *y*-coordinate is 3. The coordinates are (3, 3).

b. Point *B* is 4 units to the left of the origin and 0 units up or down. The *x*-coordinate is −4 and the *y*-coordinate is 0. The coordinates are (−4, 0).

Exercises for Example 1

Use the coordinate plane in Example 1. Give the coordinates of the point.

1. *C*   **2.** *D*   **3.** *E*

Study Guide

For use with pages 47–51

EXAMPLE 2 **Plotting Points in a Coordinate Plane**

Plot the point in a coordinate plane. Describe the location of the point.

a. $A(-2, 0)$ **b.** $B(3, -2)$ **c.** $C(1, 2)$

Solution

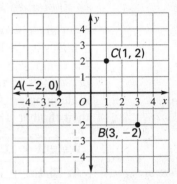

a. Begin at the origin and move 2 units to the left. Point A is on the x-axis.

b. Begin at the origin and move 3 units to the right, then 2 units down. Point B is in Quadrant IV.

c. Begin at the origin and move 1 unit to the right, then 2 units up. Point C is in Quadrant I.

Exercises for Example 2

Plot the point in a coordinate plane. Describe the location of the point.

4. $F(-5, -3)$ **5.** $G(0, 4)$ **6.** $H(-6, 2)$

EXAMPLE 3 **Making a Scatter Plot**

The data in the table show the amount of water used after the given number of minutes in a shower. Make a scatter plot of the data.

Time (minutes)	3	6	10	12	15	20
Water (gallons)	7.5	15	25	30	37.5	50

Solution

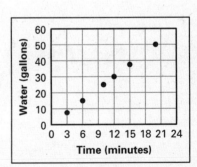

(1) Write the data as ordered pairs. Let the x-coordinate represent the time, and let the y-coordinate represent the water: (3, 7.5), (6, 15), (10, 25), (12, 30), (15, 37.5), (20, 50)

(2) Plot the ordered pairs in a coordinate plane. You need only the first quadrant.

Exercise for Example 3

7. Describe any relationship you see in the scatter plot from Example 3.

Name _____ Date _____

Real-World Problem Solving

For use with pages 47–51

Puppy Growth

Properly cared for newborn puppies rely on their mother's milk for the first couple weeks of their lives. A dog owner usually starts to wean puppies from mother's milk around 3–6 weeks after birth.

In Exercises 1–3, use the following information.

Your uncle's American bulldog has a litter of 9 puppies. There are 2 females and 7 males in the litter. You help to weigh all of the puppies. You wonder whether the comparative weights of the puppies will remain the same as they grow. You decide to test this idea on the males after 6 weeks. You record the weights of the male puppies at birth and at 6 weeks of age, while they are still nursing from their mother. The data are shown in the table below.

Weight	Dog 1	Dog 2	Dog 3	Dog 4	Dog 5	Dog 6	Dog 7
At Birth:	12 oz	14 oz	15 oz	15 oz	16 oz	16 oz	18 oz
6 weeks:	10.2 lb	11.4 lb	11.5 lb	12.4 lb	13.0 lb	12.6 lb	13.8 lb

1. Write the data as ordered pairs. Let the *x*-coordinate represent the birth weight in ounces and the *y*-coordinate represent the weight in pounds after 6 weeks.

2. Plot the coordinate pairs in a coordinate plane. Use appropriate scales for the *x*- and *y*-axes.

3. Analyze the scatter plot. Do the data points show whether the comparative weights of the pups remained the same for the first six weeks? Explain.

Name _____ Date _____

Challenge Practice

For use with pages 47–51

The point (*a*, *b*) is in Quadrant IV of a coordinate plane. Tell what quadrant the point with the given coordinates is in.

1. $(-a, |b|)$ **2.** $(|a|, -b)$ **3.** $(-b, a)$

The variables *a* and *b* represent nonzero, unequal integers. The points represented by the given coordinates are plotted and connected in order and the first point is connected to the last. Tell what type of shape is formed.

4. $(b, b), (-b, b), (-b, -b), (b, -b)$ **5.** $(a, b), (b, a), (a, a)$

6. $(-b, a), (-b, b), (0, b), (b, b), (b, a)$

7. For the following points, $a = 2b$: $(0, a), (-b, -a), (a, b), (-a, b), (b, -a)$

Data are collected for the situation described. A scatter plot is made for the data. Will the points *rise* or *fall* from left to right?

8. The distance traveled by an object moving at a constant speed is measured at different points in time. The number of seconds elapsed is represented by the *x*-axis and the overall distance traveled is represented by the *y*-axis.

9. The amount of fuel in a boat's fuel tank is recorded every fifteen minutes during a boat ride. The time passed in minutes is represented by the *x*-axis and the amount of fuel in gallons is represented by the *y*-axis.

10. An airplane's altitude is recorded every 60 seconds from take-off until landing for a flight. The time passed in minutes is represented by the *x*-axis and the altitude in meters is represented by the *y*-axis.

Name _____ Date _____

Chapter Review Games and Activities

For use after Chapter 1

Order of Operations Puzzle

Cut out the puzzle pieces and match them so that the adjacent expressions are equivalent.

Box 1
- Top: $8 - 7 \div 7$
- Left: $24 - 3 \times 4$
- Right: $(2^2) \div (5 + (-6))$
- Bottom: $2 - 18 \div 3$

Box 2
- Top: $10 \times 2 - 2 \times 8$
- Left: $48 \div 2 - 8$
- Right: $2 \times 6 - 20$
- Bottom: $-2 \times 6 - 2 \times 1$

Box 3
- Top: $-9 + 8 \div 2$
- Left: $-20 \times 4 \div 5$
- Right: $12 - 9 \div 3$
- Bottom: $6^2 - 4 \times 7$

Box 4
- Top: $2 \times 8 - 8$
- Left: $3 \times 4 - 6 \times 3$
- Right: $30 \div 5 + 5$
- Bottom: $3 + 18 \div 3$

Box 5
- Top: $1 - 10 \div 2$
- Left: $3 \times 4 - 2 \times 7$
- Right: $-8 + 4 \div 2$
- Bottom: $15 \div 5 - 2$

Box 6
- Top: $8 \times 7 - 4 \times 12$
- Left: $-1(12 - 3^2)$
- Right: $10 + 6 \div 3$
- Bottom: $1 + 3^2 \div 3$

Box 7
- Top: $2 \times 3 - 4^2$
- Left: $-14 \div 7 + 1$
- Right: $12 \div 4 \times 2 - 8$
- Bottom: $44 - 3^2 \times 4$

Box 8
- Top: $45 \div 5 + 5$
- Left: $19 - 20 \div 2$
- Right: $4^2 - 15$
- Bottom: $30 \div 5 + 1$

Box 9
- Top: $-(1 + 1) \times 1.5$
- Left: $1 - 0^2$
- Right: $(6 + 2^2 \times 2) \div 2$
- Bottom: $(7 - 10) \times 2 - 4$

Review and Projects

Name _____ Date _____

Real-Life Project: Hockey

For use after Chapter 1

Objective   Learn how integers are used for the plus/minus statistic in hockey and how it is calculated.

Materials   pencil, paper, access to the Internet or library

Investigation   *Getting Going*   When a goal is scored in a professional hockey game, each player on the ice for the team that scored gets a plus. Each player on the ice for the team that was scored against gets a minus. Throughout a season, a player's plus/minus is calculated by subtracting the number of minuses, or goals scored against, from the number of pluses, or goals scored. So, a player's plus/minus can be a positive integer, negative integer, or 0. The statistic is useful because it shows how well a player is performing both offensively and defensively. The table shows the plus/minuses of several professional hockey players.

Player	Plus/Minus	Player	Plus/Minus
Sullivan	23	Whitney	
Leetch		Cullen	−1
Dumont	−10	Carter	
Sillinger		Dowd	−14
Bondra	−2	Morrison	

Questions

1. Copy and complete the table using the following information.

   • Leetch's plus/minus is the opposite of Dowd's.
   • Carter's plus/minus is 4 more than Cullen's.
   • Whitney's plus/minus is 11 times Bondra's.
   • Sillinger's plus/minus is 25 less than Dumont's.
   • Morrison's plus/minus is 6 times Carter's.

2. Use your results from Exercise 1 to graph all of the integers on a number line. Then order them from least to greatest.

3. Which player has the lowest plus/minus? Which player has the highest?

4. Sillinger and Whitney play on the same team. Write an expression you could use to find the difference of Sillinger's and Whitney's plus/minus. What conclusion might you make about their team?

5. Looking at the table, your friend states that Sullivan must be the best hockey player of the group. Is your friend correct? Explain your reasoning.

6. A hockey player's team scores 67 goals and allows 49 goals while he is on the ice. Write an expression you could use to find the player's plus/minus. Then evaluate the expression.

7. Use the table to find the mean plus/minus.

8. Use the Internet or another reliable source to find plus/minus ratings for eight professional hockey players for the most recent season. Use both positive and negative plus/minuses. Then repeat Questions 2 and 7.

Review and Projects

Teacher's Notes for Hockey Project

For use after Chapter 1

Project Goals
- Translate verbal phrases into numerical expressions.
- Find the opposite of an integer.
- Graph integers on a number line.
- Compare and order integers.
- Add, subtract, multiply, and divide integers.
- Find a mean.

Managing the Project

Guiding Students' Work Make sure that students understand the plus/minus statistic and how it is being calculated. Encourage students to think about the questions and how they are worded so that the correct expression is written.

In Question 8, suggest to students that making a table would be helpful for gathering the data. You may choose to let the students find the statistics on their own. You can give them the names of websites such as *www.nhl.com* or *www.espn.go.com* to find the information.

Rubric for Project

The following rubric can be used to assess student work.

4 The student completes the table correctly. The number lines are neat and the integers are graphed and then ordered correctly. All of the calculations are correct. The student's solutions are clear and appropriate. The student's work is presented neatly.

3 The student completes the table correctly. The number lines and calculations may have minor mathematical errors. The student's explanations are correct, but may be a little unclear. The student's work is neat.

2 The student completes the table with a small mathematical error. The student's calculations may have more than one error. The explanations may be unclear. The student's work is incomplete or sloppy.

1 The student does not complete the table. The student's work has several mathematical errors. The explanations are unclear and incomplete. The number lines are messy. The student's work is incomplete or sloppy.

Review and Projects

Cooperative Project: Coordinate Plane Game

For use after Chapter 1

Objective **Use a coordinate plane to map a path to an object.**

Materials colored pencils or markers, graph paper, pencil

Investigation *Getting Going*   The game is for two players. In the coordinate plane shown, a ship is stranded at (20, 18). The rescue ship is at (0, 0). The goal of the game is to guide the rescue ship to the stranded ship without hitting any icebergs. The rescue ship can move horizontally or vertically, but not diagonally. The icebergs are represented by the shaded squares.

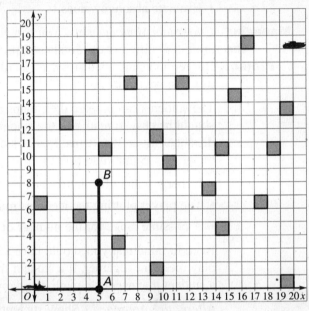

Questions

1. Name the ordered pairs that represent points *A* and *B*. What quadrant, if any, is each point located in?

2. From point *B*, can you reach the ship using only 4 moves? If so, describe the route. Then find the length of the route starting from *B*. You can find the length of a horizontal or vertical segment by counting the number of units.

3. Describe two other ways to reach the stranded ship from point *B*. Describe each route and find its length.

4. Use graph paper to copy the coordinate plane shown. Plot the stranded ship at a new point. Player 1 will arrange a specified number of icebergs on the coordinate plane and Player 2 will find a route to the stranded ship. Player 2 will then rearrange the same number of icebergs on the coordinate plane and Player 1 will find a route. The player that reaches the ship using the least number of moves wins. If the number of moves for each player is the same, determine the winner by using the length of his or her route. The player with the shorter route wins. Play several games by increasing the number of icebergs with each game. You can start the rescue ship and stranded ship at different points on the graph. Record your results from each game. Find the distance of both paths that are used to reach the ship.

5. How did you determine where to put the icebergs to make it difficult for your opponent to reach the stranded ship? Explain your reasoning.

6. What relationship would you expect to see in a scatter plot where the *x*-coordinate represents the number of icebergs and the *y*-coordinate represents the number of moves needed to reach the ship?

Review and Projects

Teacher's Notes for Coordinate Plane Game

For use after Chapter 1

Project Goals
- Plot points in the coordinate plane.
- Add and subtract integers.
- Evaluate absolute values.

Managing the Project

Classroom Management   You can encourage students to move the points around to different quadrants and move the ships farther apart or closer together. But remind students that when calculating the lengths of their routes, to always use positive numbers.

The students can prepare their maps and play simultaneously. The mapped route should be easy to read, and the students can check each other's coordinates and distances to see who wins. Markers or pens can be used to mark the routes on the graphs. Some rules you can use are:

- Icebergs cannot be plotted side by side.
- The player plotting the icebergs must always leave a possible path to the ship.
- A possible range for the number of icebergs is at least 10 and at most 30.

Keep in mind that you should have students with the same level of math skills play the game together. If a student that has difficulty with math is paired with a student that excels in math, the game may be unfair.

Alternative Approach   Show students how to use absolute value to find the length of a horizontal or vertical segment. For a horizontal segment, find the absolute value of the difference of the x-coordinates. For a vertical segment, find the absolute value of the difference of the y-coordinates. For example, the distance between $A(5, 0)$ and $B(5, 8)$ is $AB = \left| 0 - 8 \right| = \left| -8 \right| = 8$.

Rubric for Project

The following rubric can be used to assess student work.

4 The students play the game correctly—all of the answers are correct. The students answer the questions logically and insightfully. The coordinate planes are clear and neat. The students play the game successfully.

3 The students play the game correctly for the most part – most of the answers are correct. The answers to the questions are logical and somewhat insightful. The coordinate planes are neat with minor errors. The students have little difficulty playing the game.

2 The students do not correctly play the game, but an attempt is made. There are errors in the answers to the questions. There are a few errors in the coordinate planes. The coordinate planes are a little sloppy. The students do not correctly play the game as suggested, but an attempt is made.

1 The students do not correctly play the game or do not attempt to. There are many errors in the answers to the questions. The coordinate planes are incomplete or sloppy.

Review and Projects

Name _____ Date _____

Independent Extra Credit Project: Checkbook Balance

For use after Chapter 1

Objective Track the activity of a checking account and find its balance.

Materials ruler, paper, pencil

Investigation *Getting Going*   The bar graph shows the amounts of money you deposited and withdrew from your checking account.

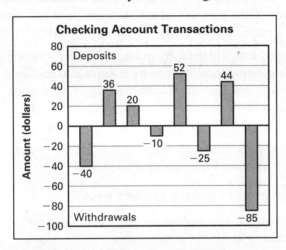

Checking Account Transactions

Questions

1. Find the difference between (a) your largest deposit and your largest withdrawal and (b) your smallest deposit and your smallest withdrawal.

2. Find the sum of the deposits and withdrawals.

3. If you had $150 in your checking account before your first transaction, how much is in your account after your last transaction?

4. If you have $120 in your account after the last transaction, determine how much was in your account before the first transaction. Explain how you found your answer.

5. Find the mean withdrawal, mean deposit, and overall mean transaction.

6. Complete the balance column in the transaction register. Write the expression you used to find each answer.

Date	Check No.	Transaction Type	Debit	Credit	Balance
					$95.00
4/10	325	Car Inspection	$43.00		
4/13		Deposit		$28.00	
4/17	326	Mrs. Wilkins	$35.00		
4/24	327	Magazine subscription	$16.00		
4/29		Deposit		$40.00	
5/4	328	Cellular phone bill	$29.00		
5/12		Deposit		$25.00	

7. On May 16, you want to write a check for $70. Is there enough money in your account?

8. Create a bar graph similar to the one above for the given transaction register.

Review and Projects

Teacher's Notes for Checkbook Balance Project

For use after Chapter 1

Project Goals
- Add, subtract, and divide integers.
- Find a mean.
- Construct a bar graph showing positive and negative integers.

Managing the Project

Guiding Students' Work It may be helpful to bring an actual transaction register and checkbook to class the day of the project and ask students questions about them so they can familiarize themselves with some of the terms, such as "debit."

Be sure that students understand that withdrawing money is similar to adding negative integers or subtracting, and depositing money is similar to adding positive integers. Encourage students to evaluate different expressions when tracking the activity of the checkbook. For example, when calculating the balance, show them that $95 - 43$ and $95 + (-43)$ give the same result.

In Question 8, you may have to review how to construct bar graphs. Pay close attention to the length of the bars when representing the integers.

Rubric for Project

The following rubric can be used to assess student work.

4 All of the calculations are correct. The student correctly completes the transaction register. In Question 8, the bar graph is clear, the bars have the same width, and are the correct length. The student's work is neat.

3 Most of the calculations are correct. The student correctly completes the transaction register but does not show the expressions. In Question 8, the bar graph is mostly correct, except for one or two minor errors. The student's work is neat.

2 The student may have some errors in the calculations. The transaction register is completed with one or two errors. In Question 8, the bar graph is completed with some errors. The work is sloppy or incomplete.

1 The student makes many errors in the calculations. The student incorrectly completes the transaction register. In Question 8, the bar graph is unclear or incomplete. The work is sloppy.

Name _____ Date _____

Cumulative Practice

For use after Chapter 1

Evaluate the expression when $a = 3$. (Lesson 1.1)

1. $a + 6$

2. $17 - a$

3. $5a$

4. $\dfrac{21}{a}$

Evaluate the expression when $x = 5$, $y = 2$, and $z = 4$. (Lesson 1.1)

5. $x + y$

6. $z - y$

7. xz

8. $\dfrac{z}{y}$

Write the product using an exponent. (Lesson 1.2)

9. $14 \cdot 14 \cdot 14$

10. $c \cdot c \cdot c \cdot c \cdot c$

11. $(3.6)(3.6)$

Write the power in words and as a repeated multiplication. Then evaluate the power. (Lesson 1.2)

12. 6^4

13. 11^3

14. $(1.8)^2$

15. 3^8

Evaluate the expression. (Lesson 1.3)

16. $14.7 + 3 \cdot 5$

17. $6 \cdot 7 - 9 \cdot 2$

18. $\dfrac{53 + 13}{8 - 5}$

19. $2(35 - 4^2)$

Evaluate the expression when $a = 7$, $b = 3$, and $c = 2$. (Lesson 1.3)

20. $0.45c + b$

21. $(a - c)^3 + b$

22. $ab - 2c$

23. $b + (10 - a)^4$

24. $(2 - c)^2 + a$

25. $3a - \dfrac{4b}{c}$

Complete the statement using $<$ or $>$. (Lesson 1.4)

26. $-5 \underline{\ ?\ } 6$

27. $4 \underline{\ ?\ } -10$

28. $-13 \underline{\ ?\ } 2$

29. $-12 \underline{\ ?\ } -7$

State the absolute value of the number. (Lesson 1.4)

30. -19

31. 8

32. -1

33. -34

Review and Projects

Cumulative Practice

For use after Chapter 1

Find the sum. (Lesson 1.5)

34. $4 + (-22)$ **35.** $-9 + 2$ **36.** $-1 + (-16)$

37. $-85 + 40$ **38.** $-10 + (-21)$ **39.** $18 + (-5)$

40. $-6 + 74$ **41.** $31 + (-61)$ **42.** $13 + (-13)$

Evaluate the expression when $x = -3$, $y = 4$, and $z = -1$. (Lesson 1.5)

43. $22 + y$ **44.** $z + y$

45. $y + (-14)$ **46.** $x + z$

47. $-8 + x$ **48.** $x + y$

49. $z + 10$ **50.** $-24 + y$

Find the difference. (Lesson 1.6)

51. $6 - (-2)$ **52.** $5 - 9$ **53.** $-1 - (-8)$

54. $21 - 46$ **55.** $-16 - (-19)$ **56.** $15 - (-9)$

57. $8 - 53$ **58.** $-30 - 12$ **59.** $17 - (-33)$

Simplify. (Lesson 1.7)

60. $-34 \div 2$ **61.** $-5(21)$

62. $-45 \div (-9)$ **63.** $10(-1)(-12)$

64. $75 \div 3(-5)$ **65.** $-3(-28) \div (-4)$

Plot the point in a coordinate plane. Describe the location of the point. (Lesson 1.8)

66. $(6, -2)$ **67.** $(-2, 3)$

68. $(-1, -4)$ **69.** $(0, 0)$

70. $(8, 5)$ **71.** $(0, -6)$

72. $(1, 7)$ **73.** $(3, 0)$

Review and Projects

Answers

Lesson 1.1

Technology Activity

1. 203 **2.** 233 **3.** 264 **4.** 29.5 **5.** 60
6. 16 **7.** (a) 65 pounds per month
(b) 15 pounds per week

Practice A

1. 11 **2.** 16 **3.** 45 **4.** 4 **5.** 17 **6.** 31
7. 50 **8.** 7 **9.** 1 **10.** 10 **11.** 12 **12.** 3
13. 7 **14.** 21 **15.** 61 **16.** 17 **17.** $n + 7$
18. $n - 11$ **19.** $\frac{n}{6}$ **20.** $n \cdot 8$ **21.** $n - 5$
22. $\frac{n}{5}$ **23.** 56 **24.** $5s$; \$75 **25.** $v + m$
26. 250; 300; 350 **27.** 176

Practice B

1. 4 **2.** 30 **3.** 14 **4.** 25 **5.** 19 **6.** 48
7. 42 **8.** 6 **9.** 90 **10.** 2 **11.** 17 **12.** 22
13. 51 **14.** 50 **15.** 160 **16.** 4 **17.** $\frac{130}{g}$
18. $27 + n$ **19.** $29 - n$ **20.** $n - 6$
21. $16 + n$ **22.** $7n$ **23.** $\frac{42}{n}$ **24.** $\frac{56}{n}$ **25.** $12n$
26.

Books	Cost (dollars)	Amount left (dollars)
1	7	343
2	14	336
3	21	329
4	28	322

27. $7b$ **28.** $350 - 7b$ **29.** 50

Practice C

1. 3.5 **2.** 3.17 **3.** 7.5 **4.** 0.3 **5.** 11
6. 37.7 **7.** 85 **8.** 20 **9.** 8 **10.** 3 **11.** 9.6
12. 132 **13.** 72 **14.** 5 **15.** 47 **16.** 0.7
17. $100x$ **18.** $\frac{p}{100}$ **19.** $60m$ **20.** $4g$
21. $2bh$; 1600 **22.** $15g$ **23.** \$270; \$195; \$360
24. $15g + c$ **25.** \$333; \$228; \$420
26. Rose, Sally, Steven

Study Guide

1. 21 **2.** 45 **3.** 15 **4.** 4 **5.** 1460 miles

6. 56 **7.** 11 **8.** 2 **9.** 3 **10.** $17 - n$
11. $\frac{n}{5}$ **12.** $n + 10$

Challenge Practice

1. 13.8 **2.** 132 **3.** 5.8 **4.** 76.8 **5.** 20.4
6. 27 **7.** 90 **8.** 88.2 **9.** 37.8
10. *Sample answer:* $p\ell + cf$, where p is the cost per foot and ℓ is the length in feet of one rope and c is the cost per foot and f is the length in feet of the other rope; \$20.48

Lesson 1.2

Practice A

1. 16^3 **2.** 18^5 **3.** $(0.4)^4$ **4.** $(1.2)^2$ **5.** c^7
6. n^8 **7.** 64 **8.** 256 **9.** 4096 **10.** 0.8
11. 0.4096 **12.** 0.64 **13.** 19 squared;
$19 \cdot 19 = 361$ **14.** 20 cubed; $20 \cdot 20 \cdot 20 = 8000$
15. 0.7 cubed; $0.7 \cdot 0.7 \cdot 0.7 = 0.343$
16. 2.4 squared; $2.4 \cdot 2.4 = 5.76$ **17.** 3.2 cubed;
$3.2 \cdot 3.2 \cdot 3.2 = 32.768$ **18.** 0.6 to the fourth
power; $0.6 \cdot 0.6 \cdot 0.6 \cdot 0.6 = 0.1296$ **19.** 11 to
the fourth power; $11 \cdot 11 \cdot 11 \cdot 11 = 14,641$
20. 9 to the fifth power; $9 \cdot 9 \cdot 9 \cdot 9 \cdot 9 = 59,049$
21. 10,000 **22.** 100,000 **23.** 1,000,000
24. 0.0144 **25.** 0.001728 **26.** 0.12
27. 196 m^2 **28.** 6.25 ft^2 **29.** 9.261 in.^{3}
30. 216 cm^3
31.

Stage	Calls made, as a power	Value of power
1	3^1	3
2	3^2	9
3	3^3	27
4	3^4	81
5	3^5	243

6561 calls have been made after stage 8.

Practice B

1. 43^4 **2.** 100^3 **3.** x^3 **4.** p^5 **5.** 64; 0.09
6. 512; 0.027 **7.** 4096; 0.0081
8. 262,144; 0.000729
9. 16,777,216; 0.00006561

Lesson 1.2 *continued*

10. 2,097,152; 0.0002187

11. 9 to the sixth power; $9 \cdot 9 \cdot 9 \cdot 9 \cdot 9 \cdot 9 = 531,441$

12. 16 to the fourth power; $16 \cdot 16 \cdot 16 \cdot 16 = 65,536$

13. 2.5 to the fourth power;
$2.5 \cdot 2.5 \cdot 2.5 \cdot 2.5 = 39.0625$

14. 1.4 cubed; $1.4 \cdot 1.4 \cdot 1.4 = 2.744$

15. 0.262144 **16.** 0.4096 **17.** 0.64

18. 3375 **19.** 50,625 **20.** 759,375

21. 289 in.^{2} **22.** 484 ft^2 **23.** 6.25 m^2

24. 0.36 cm^2 **25.** 0.729 yd^3 **26.** 2.197 ft^3

27. 27,000 cm^3 **28.** 5832 mm^3

29. The number in the first row to the fourth power, n^4, is equal to the number in the second row.

Practice C

1. 1.4 to the fifth power;
$1.4 \cdot 1.4 \cdot 1.4 \cdot 1.4 \cdot 1.4 = 5.37824$

2. 2.97 cubed; $2.97 \cdot 2.97 \cdot 2.97 = 26.198073$

3. 33 cubed; $33 \cdot 33 \cdot 33 = 35,937$

4. 40 to the sixth power;
$40 \cdot 40 \cdot 40 \cdot 40 \cdot 40 \cdot 40 = 4,096,000,000$

5. 196; 0.0324 **6.** 14; 0.18 **7.** 38,416;
0.00104976 **8.** 537,824; 0.0001889568
9. 2744; 0.005832 **10.** 7,529,536;
0.000034012224 **11.** 36 in.^{2} **12.** 64 ft^2
13. 81 cm^2 **14.** 3375 mm^3 **15.** 8 cm^3
16. 27 in.^{3} **17.** 3 **18.** 5 **19.** 6
20.

Day	Amount received, in cents, as a power	Value of the power
1	3^1	3
2	3^2	9
3	3^3	27
4	3^4	81
5	3^5	243

You earn $21.87 after 7 days.

Study Guide

1. 21^3 **2.** d^5 **3.** $(2.7)^4$ **4.** 2 to the sixth
power; $2 \cdot 2 \cdot 2 \cdot 2 \cdot 2 \cdot 2 = 64$

5. 7 to the fourth power; $7 \cdot 7 \cdot 7 \cdot 7 = 2401$

6. 0.4 cubed; $(0.4) \cdot (0.4) \cdot (0.4) = 0.064$

7. 25; 0.09 **8.** 625; 0.0081 **9.** 3125; 0.00243

10. 20.25 in.^{2} **11.** 169 cm^2 **12.** 512 m^3

13. 39.304 yd^3

Challenge Practice

1. $3^4 \cdot 4^3$ **2.** $a^3 \cdot b^2$ **3.** $(x + 2)^4$

4. $(r + s + t)^2$ **5.** 100 **6.** 81 **7.** 256

8. 2^6; 4^3 **9.** 10^6; 100^3; 1000^2

10. Both squares have side lengths of 5 inches;
one square has a side length of 1 inch and the
other square has a side length of 7 inches.

Lesson 1.3

Practice A

1. 31 **2.** 1 **3.** 37 **4.** 23 **5.** 30 **6.** 2
7. 24 **8.** 9 **9.** 3 **10.** 18 **11.** 21 **12.** 0
13. 33 **14.** 29 **15.** 16 **16.** 18 **17.** 10
18. 12 **19.** 507 **20.** 12 **21.** 77 **22.** 84
23. 2 **24.** 1.6 **25.** 3 **26.** 5
27. $3(3.99) + 2(3.8) + 1(15.99)$; $35.56
28. 91 ft^2

Practice B

1. 27.4 **2.** 21.6 **3.** 13 **4.** 5 **5.** 56
6. 1152 **7.** 65 **8.** 77.5 **9.** 2 **10.** 17
11. 19 **12.** 14 **13.** 2 **14.** 56.4 **15.** 4
16. 1.6 **17.** 55.2 **18.** 7840 **19.** 2812.6
20. 62 **21.** 26 in.^{2} **22.** 20 points
23. $1(0.99) + 16(0.1)$; $2.59

Practice C

1. 2178 **2.** 336.5 **3.** 3 **4.** 8 **5.** 4 **6.** 120
7. 53.248 **8.** 376 **9.** 581.904 **10.** 112.8
11. 155.52 **12.** 3 **13.** 50 **14.** 159 **15.** 39
16. 4.2 **17.** 76.7 **18.** 128 **19.** 2.357
20. 24.784 **21.** $416 **22.** 39 m^2

Study Guide

1. 87 **2.** 33 **3.** 2 **4.** 84 **5.** 6 **6.** 2.3
7. $88.95

Lesson 1.3 continued

Challenge Practice

1. 7 **2.** 15 **3.** $4^2 \times (13 - 9) \div 32 + 4 = 6$

4. $(12 - 5) \times (6 + 19) - 14 = 111$

5. $90 \div (3 + 7) + 3 \times 2 = 15$

6. $4 \times 10^2 - 1000 \div 5 + 4 = 204$

7. $800 - \frac{1}{2}(800) + 80 - \frac{1}{3}\left[800 - \frac{1}{2}(800) + 80\right] + \frac{1}{2}(60) = 350$; Emily is 350 meters from her house.

Lesson 1.4

Practice A

1.

$-7, -4, -3, 0, 2, 4$

2.

$-3, -2, -1, 7, 8, 9$

3.

$-7, -5, -3, 2, 6, 9$

4.

$-7, -6, -5, -1, 0, 1$

5. < **6.** > **7.** > **8.** > **9.** < **10.** <

11. 12 **12.** 17 **13.** 21 **14.** 32 **15.** 45

16. 98 **17.** -56 **18.** -37 **19.** 48 **20.** 65

21. -13 **22.** 29 **23.** 5 **24.** 8 **25.** 12

26. 10 **27.** $-5, -3, -2, 1, 3$; Jerri, Fernando, Lance, Hugh, Elinor

Practice B

1.

$-20, -14, -13, -11, -9, -7$

2.

$-30, -15, -5, 10, 20, 35$

3.

$-3, -2, -1, 0, 1, 2, 3$

4.

$-50, -30, -10, 20, 40, 60$

Practice B (cont)

5. > **6.** < **7.** > **8.** > **9.** < **10.** >

11. 73 **12.** 80 **13.** 16 **14.** 106 **15.** 34

16. 54 **17.** 98 **18.** 77 **19.** -45 **20.** -70

21. -63 **22.** 23 **23.** 7 **24.** 11 **25.** 14

26. 42 **27.** 2 **28.** 21 **29.** 4 **30.** 17

31. a. increase **b.** decrease **c.** Tuesday; Monday

Practice C

1. 11 **2.** 138 **3.** 43 **4.** 16 **5.** 151 **6.** 89

7. -119 **8.** -202 **9.** -97 **10.** 114

11. 213 **12.** 86 **13.** 24 **14.** 6 **15.** -15

16. -9 **17.** 24 **18.** 21 **19.** 6 **20.** 8

21. -15 **22.** 29 **23.** 11 **24.** 35

25. a. 6194, 4807, -12, -42 **b.** Mt. McKinley
c. Lake Eyre **d.** Bahia Blanca, Lake Eyre, Mont Blanc, Mt. McKinley

26. some values; true for any positive or negative value of a and false for $a = 0$ **27.** all values

28. some values; true for $a = 0$ and false for any positive or negative value of a

Study Guide

1.

$-9, -4, -1, 5, 16$

2.

$-11, -5, 0, 5, 17, 20$

3. 24; 24 **4.** 41; -41 **5.** 63; 63 **6.** 63

7. 0 **8.** 25

Challenge Practice

1. $-|-6|, -|5|, -2, 1, -(-3), |-4|, -(-|-7|)$ **2.** $-|22|, -|-(-21)|, -18, -|-17|, -(-17), 19, 26$ **3.** 15 **4.** 3 **5.** 15

6. -3 **7.** negative **8.** positive **9.** negative

10. positive

Lesson 1.5

Practice A

1. positive **2.** negative **3.** negative

4. negative **5.** -5 **6.** -5 **7.** -15 **8.** -18

Lesson 1.5 *continued*

9. -4 **10.** 6 **11.** -13 **12.** -7 **13.** 2
14. -67 **15.** -71 **16.** -17 **17.** 2 **18.** 8
19. -7 **20.** 15 **21.** 16 **22.** 4 **23.** 4
24. -27 **25.** -16 **26.** -1 **27.** -6
28. -17 **29.** 95, -32, 80, -25; \$118
30. 5, -3, -1, 6; 7 yards

Practice B

1. negative **2.** positive **3.** -19 **4.** -26
5. 29 **6.** -32 **7.** -36 **8.** -44 **9.** -109
10. -95 **11.** 74 **12.** -11 **13.** 12
14. -55 **15.** -74 **16.** 28 **17.** -19
18. 47 **19.** 65 **20.** -121 **21.** -1
22. -29 **23.** 76 **24.** -15 **25.** -22
26. -86 **27.** 25 **28.** 22 **29.** -53
30. -10, 6, -3, 2, -8; $-13°$F **31.** 800, 100, 150, -110, -400; \$540

Practice C

1. -46 **2.** 35 **3.** -64 **4.** -76 **5.** 9
6. -12 **7.** -203 **8.** -32 **9.** 22 **10.** -37
11. -6 **12.** 0 **13.** -10 **14.** -65 **15.** -13
16. 46 **17.** -40 **18.** 96 **19.** -54 **20.** -16
21. -41 **22.** -49 **23.** -71 **24.** 32 **25.** 59
26. -88 **27.** 18 **28.** 9 **29.** -7
30. a. negative **b.** positive **c.** negative
31. a.

Transaction	Balance
1	\$68
2	\$51
3	\$31
4	\$81
5	\$91
6	\$76
7	\$52
8	\$23
9	$-\$8$
10	$-\$13$

b. $-\$13$ **c.** yes, transactions 9 and 10

Study Guide

1. -3 **2.** -17 **3.** -6 **4.** 18 **5.** -42
6. -21 **7.** -3 **8.** 13 **9.** -38 **10.** -31
11. 5 **12.** 1

Real-World Problem Solving

1. $-85 + (-4) + (-55) + (-27) + 9 + (-22)$
2. -184 **3.** $203 + (-184) = 19$; The total of the estimates is 19 feet less than the actual vertical distance.

Challenge Practice

1. 469 **2.** -4785 **3.** a is positive, b can be any integer.
4. (1) Both a and b are positive, or (2) a and b are negative and $a = b$.
5. One of the integers a and b is positive, the other is negative.
6. (1) Both a and b are positive, or (2) both a and b are negative. **7.** a and b are opposites.
8. One of the integers a and b is positive, the other is negative. The absolute value of the positive integer is 1 greater than the absolute value of the negative integer.
9. (1) Both a and b are negative, or (2) one is negative, the other is positive, and the absolute value of the negative integer is greater than the absolute value of the positive integer.
10. (1) a is positive and b is negative, or (2) a and b are both positive and a is greater than b, or (3) a and b are both negative and the absolute value of b is greater than the absolute value of a.

Lesson 1.6

Activity Master

1. -4 **2.** 5 **3.** -20 **4.** 11 **5.** -5
6. -10 **7.** -14 **8.** -6 **9.** 7 **10.** -4
11. 17 **12.** -7
13. If the second integer is greater than the first integer, the difference will be *negative*. Example: $-4 - (-2) = -2$; If the second integer is less than the first integer, the difference will be *positive*. Example: $-2 - (-6) = 4$; If the integers are equal, the difference will be *zero*. Example: $-3 - (-3) = 0$

Lesson 1.6 *continued*

Practice A

1. −3   2. −4   3. 10   4. 17   5. −12
6. −15   7. 9   8. −2   9. −11   10. −14
11. −3   12. −13   13. 2   14. −18   15. 17
16. 19°C   17. 18°C   18. 23°F   19. 44°F
20. 35 ft   21. 52 yd   22. −32 m   23. −8 m
24. 2   25. 1   26. 24°F   27. −6125 ft
28. 22°F

Practice B

1. −4   2. −11   3. 24   4. 21   5. −21
6. −47   7. 22   8. −13   9. −15   10. −11
11. 43   12. 3   13. −24   14. −21   15. 9
16. −27   17. 11   18. −1   19. 39°C
20. 9°C   21. −21°F   22. −11°F   23. 24 m
24. 70 m   25. −165 yd   26. −16 ft   27. −11
28. −161   29. −721 ft; A negative value means
the hikers are going down. A positive value means
the hikers are going up.   30. −22°F

Practice C

1. 5   2. −14   3. 78   4. 63   5. −62
6. −115   7. −37   8. 25   9. −19   10. −44
11. 29   12. 62   13. 18   14. −64   15. 24
16. −51°C   17. −68°F   18. −16 m
19. −125 ft   20. −43   21. −421   22. −62
23. 270   24. 25   25. 9   26. −4   27. −10
28. $101,200   29. a. $58,000   b. $214,000
c. $46,000   d. $318,000   e. $208,000

Study Guide

1. −9   2. −13   3. 20   4. 8   5. 23   6. −15
7. −11   8. 25   9. 39°C   10. −12°F
11. 83 ft   12. −104 m

Challenge Practice

1. −5   2. −35   3. 4   4. −33   5. negative
6. positive   7. could be either
8. could be either
9. 76,112 − 227 − 34 − 1373 − 5 + 325
= 74,798; The new account balance is about
$74,798.

Lesson 1.7

Practice A

1. negative   2. positive   3. negative
4. negative   5. positive   6. negative   7. 104
8. −170   9. 0   10. −90   11. −60   12. 126
13. −25   14. 0   15. −3   16. 14   17. −4
18. −5   19. 396   20. −288   21. 1960
22. 6   23. 3   24. −10   25. −9   26. 60
27. −18   28. 40°F   29. $35

Practice B

1. negative   2. negative   3. positive
4. −125   5. 116   6. −4   7. −7   8. 6
9. −288   10. 252   11. −3   12. 34
13. −63   14. −133   15. 231   16. −960
17. 8320   18. 5   19. 4   20. 32   21. −81
22. <   23. >   24. 15   25. −6   26. −5°C

Practice C

1. −8   2. 3   3. 175   4. −396   5. −1456
6. 528   7. −7   8. −75   9. −53   10. −26
11. −4402   12. −1239   13. 2255
14. −4320   15. 2   16. −8   17. −30   18. 5
19. 672   20. −1296   21. −4320   22. −9
23. −36   24. −4   25. 6   26. 19   27. 498 ft
28. 2; 3.5; the mean represents a lower number of
yards gained.

Study Guide

1. 54   2. −13   3. 3   4. 88   5. −20
6. −135   7. 84 feet below sea level   8. −10
9. −18

Challenge Practice

1. 21   2. 8   3. 14   4. −6   5. 6   6. 49
7. $2800   8. $1600   9. −$560; a negative
profit means that the company lost money.
10. −$80

Copyright © McDougal Littell/Houghton Mifflin Company
All rights reserved.

Pre-Algebra   **A5**
Chapter 1   Resource Book

Lesson 1.8

Practice A

1. $(-4, 3)$ **2.** $(-1, 2)$ **3.** $(1, 1)$ **4.** $(-2, 0)$

5. $(2, -1)$ **6.** $(-3, -3)$ **7.** $(0, -4)$

8. $(3, -3)$

9. Quadrant III

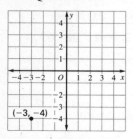

10. Quadrant IV

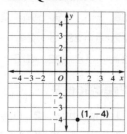

11. Quadrant IV

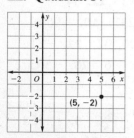

12. x-axis

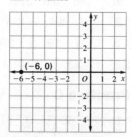

13. Quadrant IV

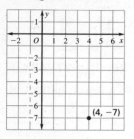

14. Quadrant IV

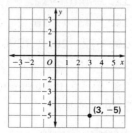

15. Quadrant II

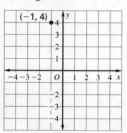

16. Quadrant II

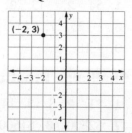

17. Quadrant III

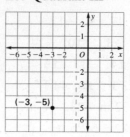

18. a.

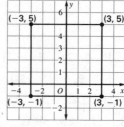

b. The figure is a square, because it has 4 sides of equal length.

19. a.

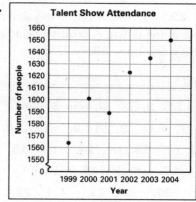

b. As the years increase, the talent show attendance tends to increase.

20. a.

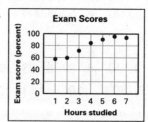

b. As the number of hours spent studying increases, the exam score tends to increase.

Practice B

1. $(0, -3)$ **2.** $(1, -1)$ **3.** $(4, -4)$

4. $(-4, 1)$ **5.** $(-2, 2)$ **6.** $(2, 4)$ **7.** $(2, 0)$

8. $(-3, -1)$

Lesson 1.8 *continued*

9. Quadrant II

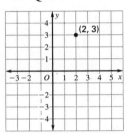

10. Quadrant III

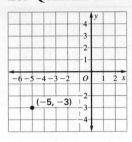

11. Quadrant I

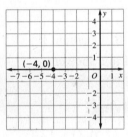

12. Quadrant I

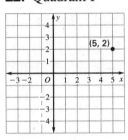

13. *x*-axis

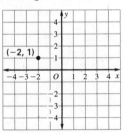

14. Quadrant IV

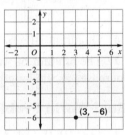

15. Quadrant II

16. *x*-axis

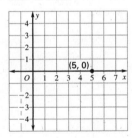

17. *y*-axis

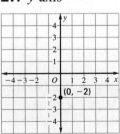

18. a.

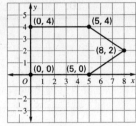

b. The figure is a pentagon, because it has 5 sides.

19. a.

x	−3	−2	−1	0	1	2	3
y	−10	−7	−4	−1	2	5	8

b. (−3, −10), (−2, −7), (−1, −4), (0, −1), (1, 2), (2, 5), (3, 8)

c.

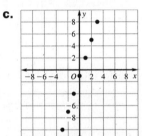

d. The points form a straight line.

20. a.

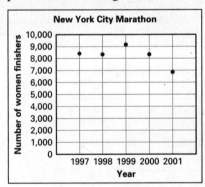

b. The number of women finishing the New York City Marathon increased slightly from 1997 to 1999, then decreased slightly from 1999 to 2001.

Practice C

1. (−8, 2)　**2.** (0, 6)　**3.** (6, 5)　**4.** (−5, 0)

5. (2, 1)　**6.** (−2, −2)　**7.** (7, −6)

8. (0, −7)

9. Quadrant III

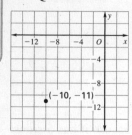

10. Quadrant I

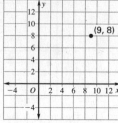

11. Quadrant I

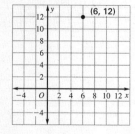

12. Quadrant II

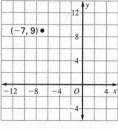

13. Quadrant IV

14. Quadrant IV

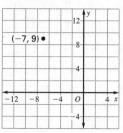

15. a.

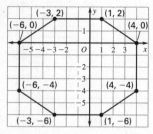

b. The figure is an octagon, because it has 8 sides.

16. a.

x	−3	−2	−1	0	1	2	3
y	11	9	7	5	3	1	−1

b. (−3, 11), (−2, 9), (−1, 7), (0, 5), (1, 3), (2, 1), (3, −1)

c.

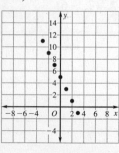

d. The points form a straight line.

17. a.

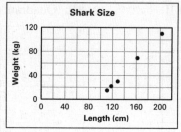

b. As the length of the shark increases, the weight of the shark increases.

Study Guide

1. (1, −4) **2.** (0, −2) **3.** (−2, 4)

4–6.

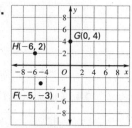

4. Quadrant III **5.** *y*-axis **6.** Quadrant II

7. The amount of water used in a shower increases as the length of time increases.

Real-World Problem Solving

1. (12, 10.2), (14, 11.4), (15, 11.5), (15, 12.4), (16, 13), (16, 12.6), (18, 13.8)

2.

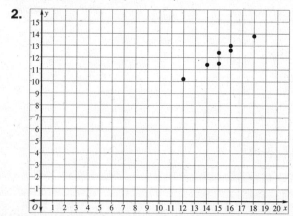

3. Yes; the point with the largest *x*-value has the largest *y*-value, so the heaviest puppy remained heaviest. The point with the smallest *x*-value has the smallest *y*-value, so the lightest puppy remained lightest. In general, the points show that the way the puppies' weights compared at birth is about the same way they compared at 6 weeks old.

Lesson 1.8 *continued*

Challenge Practice

1. Quadrant II **2.** Quadrant I **3.** Quadrant I

4. a square **5.** a triangle **6.** a rectangle

7. a star **8.** The points rise from left to right.

9. The points fall from left to right.

10. *Sample answer:* The points rise at the left most part of the coordinate plane (the airplane's ascent), level-off midway though the flight, and fall toward the right most part (the airplane's descent).

Review and Projects

Chapter Review Games and Activities

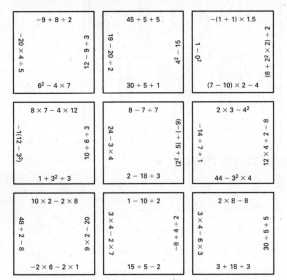

Real-Life Project

1.

Player	Plus/Minus	Player	Plus/Minus
Sullivan	23	Whitney	−22
Leetch	14	Cullen	−1
Dumont	−10	Carter	3
Sillinger	−35	Dowd	−14
Bondra	−2	Morrison	18

2.

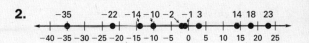

The order from least to greatest is -35, -22, -14, -10, -2, -1, 3, 14, 18, and 23.

3. Because -35 is on the far left of the number line, Sillinger has the lowest plus/minus. Because 23 is on the far right of the number line, Sullivan has the highest plus/minus.

4. $-22 - (-35) = -22 + 35 = 13$; Both players have very low plus/minuses, so you might conclude that the team they play for is not very good.

5. Sullivan may be the best hockey player, but you cannot conclude that just from the information in the table. He could be an average player on a very good team.

6. $67 - 49$ or $67 + (-49)$; 18 **7.** -2.6

8. Check student's work.

Cooperative Project

1. $A(5, 0)$; $B(5, 8)$; Point A is located on the x-axis, so it is not in any quadrant. Point B is located in Quadrant I.

2.

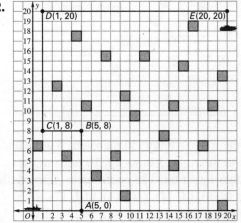

Yes; The route moves 4 units to the left, 12 units up, 19 units to the right, then 2 units down. The coordinates of the path include $(1, 8)$, $(1, 20)$, and $(20, 20)$. The length of the path is 37 units.

Review and Projects *continued*

Answers

3. *Sample answers:*

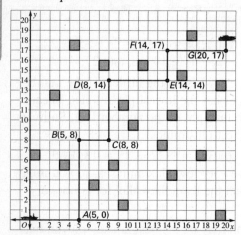

The route moves 3 units to the right, 6 units up, 6 units to the right, 3 units up, 6 units to the right, then 1 unit up. The coordinates of the path include (8, 8), (8, 14), (14, 14), (14, 17), and (20, 17). The length of the path is 25 units.

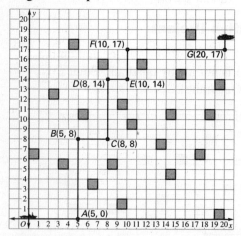

The route moves 3 units to the right, 6 units up, 2 units to the right, 3 units up, 10 units to the right, then 1 unit up. The coordinates of the path include (8, 8), (8, 14), (10, 14), (10, 17), and (20, 17). The length of the path is 25 units.

4. Check students' work.   **5.** Answers will vary.

6. As the number of icebergs increases, the number of moves needed to reach the ship should increase.

Independent Extra Credit Project

1. a. $137   **b.** $30   **2.** −$8   **3.** $142

4. $128; You can find the beginning balance by working backwards.

5. Mean withdrawal = −$40
Mean deposit = $38
Mean transaction = −$1

6.

Debit	Credit	Balance	
		$95.00	
$43.00		$52.00	← 95 + (−43) or 95 − 43
	$28.00	$80.00	← 52 + 28
$35.00		$45.00	← 80 + (−35) or 80 − 35
$16.00		$29.00	← 45 + (−16) or 45 − 16
	$40.00	$69.00	← 29 + 40
$29.00		$40.00	← 69 + (−29) or 69 − 29
	$25.00	$65.00	← 40 + 25 = 65

7. The balance in your account is $65. Because 65 < 70, you cannot write a check for $70.

8.

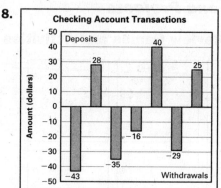

Cumulative Practice

1. 9   **2.** 14   **3.** 15   **4.** 7   **5.** 7   **6.** 2   **7.** 20

8. 2   **9.** 14^3 **10.** c^5 **11.** $(3.6)^2$

12. six to the fourth power; $6 \cdot 6 \cdot 6 \cdot 6 = 1296$

13. eleven to the third power; $11 \cdot 11 \cdot 11 = 1331$

14. one point eight to the second power; one point eight squared; $(1.8) \cdot (1.8) = 3.24$

15. three to the eighth power; $3 \cdot 3 \cdot 3 \cdot 3 \cdot 3 \cdot 3 \cdot 3 \cdot 3 = 6561$

16. 29.7   **17.** 24   **18.** 22   **19.** 38   **20.** 3.9

21. 128   **22.** 17   **23.** 84   **24.** 7   **25.** 15

26. <   **27.** >   **28.** <   **29.** <   **30.** 19   **31.** 8

32. 1   **33.** 34   **34.** −18   **35.** −7   **36.** −17

37. −45   **38.** −31   **39.** 13   **40.** 68

41. −30   **42.** 0   **43.** 26   **44.** 3   **45.** −10

46. −4   **47.** −11   **48.** 1   **49.** 9   **50.** −20

51. 8   **52.** −4   **53.** 7   **54.** −25   **55.** 3

56. 24   **57.** −45   **58.** −42   **59.** 50

60. −17   **61.** −105   **62.** 5   **63.** 120

64. −125   **65.** −21

Review and Projects *continued*

66–73.

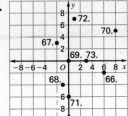

66. Quadrant IV   **67.** Quadrant II

68. Quadrant III   **69.** Origin   **70.** Quadrant I

71. *y*-axis   **72.** Quadrant I   **73.** *x*-axis